ON SAFARI
IN EAST AFRICA

Also from Collins Natural History

ON SAFARI IN EAST AFRICA

A Background Guide

Ernest Neal

HarperCollins*Publishers*

HarperCollins*Publishers*
London · Glasgow · Sydney · Auckland
Toronto · Johannesburg

First published in 1991
© Ernest Neal, 1991

ISBN 0 00 219928 9

Printed and bound in Britain
by Butler and Tanner Ltd, Frome

Contents

Acknowledgements

During the last few decades, a large number of field biologists have made ecological and behavioural studies of the fauna and flora of East Africa. Together, they have built up an ever-increasing understanding of inter-relationships within the region: without their researches this book could not have been written. I acknowledge with much gratitude the inspiration derived from their writings and my indebtedness to them for the mine of information they have so painstakingly acquired and made freely available.

I would like to select for special thanks two authors whose stimulating ideas have been particularly helpful; first, Harvey Croze, whose outstanding book *Pyramids of Life* was, in my opinion, the first really good book at a 'popular level' to treat the East African flora and fauna from a broad and truly ecological standpoint; second, the late Hugh Cott, good friend and fellow guest lecturer on many Swan's Safaris, for his book *Looking at Animals – a Zoologist in Africa*, which successfully combined scientific excellence with creative art. Others, whose books and scientific papers have been of great benefit, include Brian Bertram, the late Leslie Brown, David Cummings, Keith Eltringham, George Frame, Aadje Geertsema, Jane Goodall, Hans Kruuk, Richard Laws, David Macdonald, Cynthia Moss, Norman Myers, Robin Pellew, the late Jon Rood, Thelma Rowell, Dan Rubenstein, Jonathan Scott, Barbara Smuts, Clive Spinage and Anthony Smith. My sincere thanks to all of them and apologies to any others whose names I have inadvertently omitted.

I would also like to thank most warmly those who have helped more directly in the production of this book – in particular, David Bygott and his wife Jeannette Hanby who gave much encouragement, critically read the whole manuscript, made numerous corrections and suggestions and provided me with useful data through the excellent guides to the National Parks of Tanzania which they helped to produce; their assistance was invaluable. I am also very grateful to Jonathan Kingdon and Bob Savage who kindly read certain chapters and gave freely of their expertise, and to Michael Woods who took much time and trouble over reading the whole manuscript, making many helpful suggestions. Any errors that remain are of my own making!

I also thank the producers and camera teams involved in the production of the magnificent television programmes on East African wildlife – these provided many interesting details; in particular, to the BBC Natural History Unit for *The Tree of Thorns* programme, written and produced by Barry Payne, which I drew upon as an example of inter-relationships. I am also particularly grateful to Les Grandy who did the illustrations.

Finally, I would like to thank members of my family for their help and support, especially my wife, Betty, who shared with me the delights of numerous safaris, encouraged me over the writing and helped in so many ways.

Preface

Anyone going on safari to East Africa for the first time should be warned of the danger of addiction! Once you have experienced the welcome of the people, the vast expanses, the changing skies, the lakes and mountains and above all, the unparalleled numbers and diversity of large animals, you will want to return again and again. You have been warned!

When you arrive, you have a curious feeling you are coming home. Perhaps there is something deep down in our nature that reminds us that this was our ancestral home way back in the mists of time; for it was from here that humans dispersed, and eventually spread to all parts of the globe. During the past 10,000 years, various races have been coming back in migratory waves, mainly from the Nile basin, the Horn of Africa and from the west of the continent. More recently invasions have also come from the sea by Arabs, Persians, Indians, Indonesians and Europeans. All have influenced the development of East Africa as we know it now. Today, only small pockets of the indigenous hunter-gatherers remain.

A safari can be a wonderful experience; not least, because it gives the visitor a chance to let the sense of wonder take over from twentieth century sophistication. A safari also helps to put humanity in perspective – as part of nature, not apart from it.

There are a number of good field guides for the identification of the birds, mammals, butterflies, flowers and so on, but this book is for the reader who wants background information about what is seen – the general ecology, behaviour and adaptations of the commoner species. Seeing the animals in their natural habitats is a memorable experience, and this is greatly enhanced if you understand why a species is found in a particular place, why it is behaving in that curious way, how it interacts with other members of its own kind and to those of different species, and how it has become so superbly adapted in structure, physiology and through its behaviour to take its place in the ecosystem. It is to enable the visitor to answer some of these questions that this guide has been written and in the hope that it may make a safari more meaningful and enjoyable.

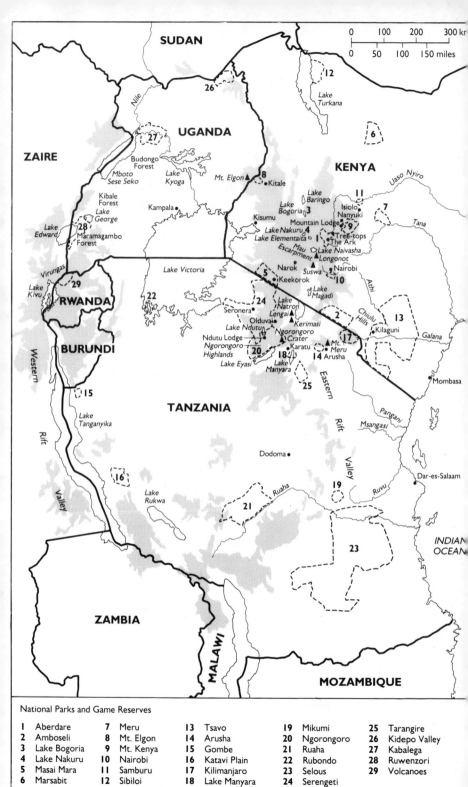

0   100   200   300 km
0 50   100   150 miles

SUDAN

UGANDA

ZAIRE

KENYA

Nile

12

Lake Turkana

26

27

6

Budongo Forest

Mboto Sese Seko

Mt. Elgon ▲ 8
• Kitale

Uaso Nyiro

11

Lake Kyoga

Kibale Forest

Lake George

Kampala •

Lake Baringo

Lake Bogoria 3

Isiolo
Nanyuki

7

Tana

Lake Edward

Maramagambo Forest

28

Kisumu •

Mountain Lodge
Lake Nakuru 4
Lake Elementaita 1

9

Tree-tops
The Ark

Lake Naivasha
Longonot

Virungas

Lake Kivu

29

RWANDA

Lake Victoria

Narok •
Keekorok •

Mau
Escarpment

Suswa ▲

Nairobi •
10

Athi

Western

BURUNDI

22

24

5

Lake Natron
Lengai

Lake Magadi

2

Chiulu
Hills

13

Seronera •

Olduvai

Kerimasi ▲

Kilaguni

Galana

15

Lake Tanganyika

TANZANIA

Lake Ndutu

Ndutu Lodge
Ngorongoro
Highlands

Ngorongoro
Crater

Karatu •

18

20

Lake Eyasi

Mt.
Meru ▲
Arusha •
14

17

25

Mombasa •

Rift

Eastern

Pangani

Msangasi

16

Lake Rukwa

Dodoma •

21

Ruaha

19

Rift

Valley

Ruvu

Dar-es-Salaam •

INDIAN
OCEAN

23

ZAMBIA

MALAWI

MOZAMBIQUE

National Parks and Game Reserves

1	Aberdare	7	Meru	13	Tsavo	19	Mikumi	25	Tarangire
2	Amboseli	8	Mt. Elgon	14	Arusha	20	Ngorongoro	26	Kidepo Valley
3	Lake Bogoria	9	Mt. Kenya	15	Gombe	21	Ruaha	27	Kabalega
4	Lake Nakuru	10	Nairobi	16	Katavi Plain	22	Rubondo	28	Ruwenzori
5	Masai Mara	11	Samburu	17	Kilimanjaro	23	Selous	29	Volcanoes
6	Marsabit	12	Sibiloi	18	Lake Manyara	24	Serengeti		

CHAPTER 1

An Introduction to East Africa

Geographical and climatic changes

To understand the origins of the present fauna of East Africa, it is useful to know something about the main changes that have occurred during the past 25 million years. It is not the details that are important in this context, but the broad geographical and climatic changes that help to clarify this astonishing picture of dynamic evolution.

25 million years ago, East Africa would have looked totally different from today. Then, in Western Kenya, for example, there were mountains where there are plains today, and in other regions where there were plains, great mountains such as Kilimanjaro now stand. It is difficult to comprehend, with our limited time scale, that such major changes to the landscape could have occurred through natural forces, with even the mountains being here today and gone tomorrow, when considered in geological terms.

The earth's lower crust consists of a number of rigid tectonic plates which float in very slow motion on a hot, partially molten layer. In places where these plates meet, the earth's upper layers may be disturbed in a most spectacular manner. If the plates collide, mountain ranges may be thrown up, and these enormous upheavals may be accompanied by volcanic activity. In addition, as a result of enormous forces beneath the crust, the earth's surface may be stretched or bulged causing weaknesses and faults. Most of East Africa has been subjected to similar powerful forces during the past 40 million years, causing the spectacular faulting of the Great Rift, the thrusting up of huge mountains such as Mount Kenya and Kilimanjaro, and the raising of much of the inland area to between one and two thousand metres.

The formation of the Great Rift

Rift formation has been a fairly continuous process, over the past 40 million years, although most activity occurred during the past 25 million. This jagged crack in the earth's surface stretches roughly N-S for 6,000 kilometres. It can be traced through the Jordan valley in the Middle East, through the Red Sea, across the highlands of Ethiopia, right through Kenya and Tanzania, to peter out in the Lower Zambezi region of Mozambique. Its largest branch, the Western Rift, diverges from it, taking a more westerly course, northwards; it marks the boundary between Zaire and East Africa.

The simplest concept of the Great Rift's formation, is that it arose when a narrow section of the earth's crust sank between parallel faults, ranging from 40–100 kilometres apart. This type of faulting certainly happened in some areas, and is particularly evident in regions where the land was raised to form huge "domes". In these areas tensions within the crust were maximised. There are places where it is possible to get spectacular views of this faulting showing both escarpments with the valley floor between. One such view-point can be reached on the road from Nairobi to Naivasha. The road climbs steadily out of Nairobi through intensively cultivated Kikuyu country into the upland forest. Then, with dramatic suddenness, you find yourself on the sharp edge of the escarpment with the valley 500 metres below stretching to the dimly seen Mau, or Western escarpment on the other side. The volcanoes, Longonot and Suswa rise majestically from the valley floor.

But not everywhere is the scene so like a textbook description. Further south, for example, Lake Manyara Hotel is perched on the edge of the western escarpment which drops dramatically to the National Park in the valley below. But in this part of the rift there is no eastern escarpment as no great faulting occurred on that side. Again, if you visit the Lake Bogoria region in Kenya, the eastern escarpment rises to impressive heights from the edge of the lake, but instead of a western escarpment caused by a single fault, a number of smaller ones have occurred, forming more minor cliffs and undulations.

10

Bearing these various exceptions in mind, it is necessary to modify the simpler concept of rift formation. First, it was not a single event, but the result of an extremely complex series of faults spanning millions of years. These surface faults reflect deep linear features in the lower crust which extend for thousands of kilometres north and south. Second, during the long history of its formation, volcanoes, over much of its eastern range were periodically belching forth lava and ash, greatly modifying the effect of the rifting by massive in-filling; in some parts of the valley these deposits are several kilometres thick. Lastly, there has been the additional modification of the landscape caused by erosion. This relentless wearing away of the rocks has greatly changed the contours, rounding off many of the hills and mountains.

It is typical of the rift that its course can be traced by the string of narrow lakes which thread their way within it: Turkana, Baringo, Bogoria, Nakuru, Elmenteita, Naivasha, Magadi, Natron and Manyara. All these lakes of the Eastern Rift arose as closed basins in the valley floor in which water from the mountains could lie. These eastern lakes are shallow, due partly to the constant raining down of volcanic material. By contrast, there was less volcanic activity in the region of the Western Rift and the lakes within it are deeper: Albert, Edward, Kivu, and the deepest of all, Tanganyika. In the latter, the escarpment falls steeply into its watery depths for 1433 metres, the lake bottom being 619 metres below sea level.

The rifting is still going on. In the north, the Red Sea is widening at a rate of 2·5 cm a year; not very much at first sight, but in a million years at the same rate, it could be as much as 25 km. Perhaps, one day, sea water will flood large areas of the valley, causing what we now know as East Africa to be isolated from the rest of the continent as Madagascar was in the past. But that will not happen tomorrow.

The rising of the great mountains

During the whole of these 25 million years, volcanic activity has been most marked, although some of the most spectacular eruptions, such as Mt. Kenya, Mt. Meru and Kilimanjaro only took place during the past few million. Mt. Kenya was at one time much higher than it is today – probably about 7,000 m. Its jagged, snow-covered peaks are the remnants of the rocks from the volcano's core, which are harder because the molten material never emerged and so cooled more slowly. This hard plug has withstood the powers of erosion much better than the softer rocks formed from the laval streams down the volcano's sides. Kilimanjaro is more recent. This great volcanic mass had three origins. The first was Shira to the west, which is now greatly eroded; Mawenzi erupted next and stands high and jagged to the east, and this is connected by a saddle to the most recent upthrust, Kibo, which still retains its crater, now surrounded by ice and snow. One of the most remarkable views of Kibo can be obtained from Amboseli on a clear night when the moon is full. Its snow-covered summit is clearly seen in the moonlight, but the dark base is invisible, so the top seems to float eerily in the sky. Quite magical.

Many volcanic craters, large and small, dot the East African countryside. The majority of these are greatly eroded and extinct, but others are clearly only dormant as they show occasional jets of steam or bubblings of mud. However, only a few are sufficiently active to suggest further eruptions may be imminent.

Of the active ones, Mt. Lengai, in northern Tanzania, is a most spectacular mountain of perfect symmetry. It last had a major eruption in 1966 when huge molten rivers of lava poured down its side and clouds of ash were ejected into the sky. Now, it stands stark and forbidding as a backdrop to Lake Natron, its crater bubbling periodically with molten material as if impatient to explode once more.

The Virungas, just over the border in east Zaire, include two active volcanoes, Nyamaragira and Nyiragongo which have had several minor eruptions in recent years. At night, from as far away as Ruwenzori National Park, you can sometimes see the red reflection of the fiery contents of their craters on low clouds above these mountains.

Of the dormant volcanoes, Longonot, near L. Naivasha, is probably the most accessible and easiest to climb. The effort involved is greatly rewarded as views from the top are spectacular. The symmetry of the crater rim is most striking, and standing on its edge, you can look down into the crater, now filled with vegetation, and see jets of steam emerge from its steep sides. Signs of its most recent eruption are plainly visible if you look down the north-western flanks of the volcano. The eruption occurred when pressure built up and a vent formed in the side causing a parasite cone to develop. From above, you can see very clearly where a broad laval stream flowed down the volcano from this new crater, as the vegetation that has colonised it is markedly different from that which surrounds it.

You can see signs of 'recent' volcanic activity if you visit Tsavo National Park. One small volcano, Shitani, in the Chyulu hills, not far from Kilaguni Lodge, may have erupted only about 400 years ago. It is possible to follow a fair-weather track which takes you into the hills and to the foot of a spectacular flow of raw lava which flowed from its crater. Even after 400 years, no vegetation has been able to get a foothold here, but in other parts of this park you can see many older flows in various stages of colonisation. On some of these you may catch a glimpse of the dainty klipspringer antelope which uses the flows as a safe retreat from predators. Klipspringers have the advantage as they can leap across the jagged terrain with speed and confidence, their rubbery hooves giving them an excellent grip.

Hot springs, where boiling mud or sulphurous steam come to the surface, may be found in many regions of the Great Rift. Those near Hell's Gate, near Naivasha, are now more difficult to visit as they are used to supply energy through a geothermal plant, but the ones at Lake Bogoria are well worth visiting. They should be approached with caution.

When Ngorongoro volcano reached its maximum size 2·5 million years ago, it may well have been as much as 6,000 m high. When it erupted, an enormous amount of material was emitted which now forms part of the Crater Highlands. Eventually, when the last eruption ceased, the magma remaining was sucked back and the entire upper portion of the cone collapsed inwards. Ngorongoro is the largest collapsed crater, or caldera, in Africa, being 15 km in diameter and with walls up to 600 m high. The crater itself is a marvellous microcosm of East African wildlife. The descent in four-wheeled drive gives you remarkable panoramic views, and when you begin to explore this vast amphitheatre of over 300 km^2 with its plains and hills, forest, lake and marshes, it is difficult to imagine that you are actually inside what was once a huge volcano.

When eruptions occur, apart from the lava flows, great volumes of ash are ejected into the sky and the finer particles may be carried on the wind for vast distances. The short-grass plains of the Serengeti were formed in this way when Mt. Kerimasi experienced a series of eruptions smothering the land with layer after layer of ash. Only the spectacular kopjes, which stand out so starkly from the plain, bear witness to the presence of the ancient rocks beneath. Sometimes, a deposit of ash may consolidate to form a hard layer, and with further deposits of softer ash on top, it becomes a hard pan below the surface soil. This has happened in the Serengeti; so the superficial layers, which are very fertile, allow the fibrous, shallow-rooted grasses to flourish, but the hard pan below is a barrier which large roots cannot penetrate. This is the main reason why trees are scarce or absent over these vast plains.

13

Climatic changes

Over the past 25 million years climatic changes have greatly influenced the evolution of the fauna. During this time it is estimated that there have been no less than 22 major climatic fluctuations as well as many of more minor significance. Although such changes tend to be gradual, each has brought evolutionary pressures to bear on animal populations. Major variations in climate brought differences in the vegetation, and animals had to adjust to these changes if they were to survive. Thus, over this period the mammalian fauna has evolved dramatically – a continual panorama of change with a host of new species taking the places of those which could no longer cope and became extinct.

Variation in rainfall has been the major factor in causing changes in the vegetation and this in turn has affected the evolution of the fauna. A high annual rainfall favours forest formation, a very low one results in desert conditions and between these extremes grassland can flourish.

Grass has played a leading role in the evolution of the larger mammals. 25 million years ago, grass had already become the dominant ground vegetation in many areas, and integrated with it was a wide range of broad-leaved herbaceous plants. Together, they provided an abundant source of food for the herbivores to exploit. During periods when the climate was particularly wet the areas of grassland contracted and the forests expanded, but compared with western and central parts of the continent, East Africa has always been drier, so even during the wettest periods there were extensive areas where grassland could persist.

One of the wettest periods was around 25–20 million years ago when rain forest was the dominant habitat type over much of the region, but even then large areas of grassland remained where herbivore evolution could continue. Many groups of mammals were represented during this period. In the more grassy areas ancestors of our present-day hyraxes were common, one species being as big as a medium-sized antelope. Primitive ruminants were there too and several kinds of proboscids, a group which later gave rise to elephants. Some proboscids were already developing trunks and some had tusks in both jaws; rhinos and forerunners of giraffes were also present. There were many forms of predators too, including ancestral forms of both dogs and cats. In the forests there were species allied to bushbabies, primitive apes and various kinds of monkey; hedgehogs, shrews and rodents were there too.

During the next 10 million years, in spite of many fluctuations the trend was for much drier conditions to exist with long periods when woody savannah was the dominant habitat type over much of the region. Forests were always present, but they were continually contracting into smaller patches and then expanding again with the fluctuations in rainfall. This caused forest species to be repeatedly isolated and re-united – an important factor influencing their evolution. During this period ground-dwelling browsers greatly increased in number and variety, and bovids, a group which includes antelopes, gazelles and buffaloes, were slowly developing into what was later to become the major constituent of the savannah fauna. Towards the end of this period, fossil finds in western Kenya showed the presence of true antelopes, recognisable giraffes and an important hominid – perhaps one of our extremely remote ancestors – *Ramapithecus*.

Little is known about the climate and fauna of the next 5 million years or so, as few fossils have been found, but much more information is available about the following 4–5 million which brings us to the present. This period which includes the late Pliocene and the Pleistocene was marked by cataclysmic disturbances: there was much volcanic activity, the building of huge mountains, severe rifting and the further raising of inland areas to as much as 2000 m in parts of Kenya. During this time the climate was subjected to extreme fluctuations.

Five million years ago the climate was probably fairly similar to what it is today with a comparable mosaic of vegetational types present. This gradually gave way to a hot, dry period which brought arid conditions to many parts, and this was followed by a considerably wetter and cooler period. The climate during the last 1–2 million years was greatly influenced by the great upheavals that occurred in East Africa at that time and also the glaciations that were then taking place in the northern hemisphere.

Glaciations had the effect of lowering the temperature in the Atlantic which meant there was less evaporation and hence less rain in Africa, and with the colder temperatures, more moisture was locked up as ice on high mountains causing glaciers on Mt. Kenya and Kilimanjaro to come down as low as 3,000 m. The interglacials, by contrast, brought warmer and wetter conditions to the region and montane forest was able to spread so much that at one time it covered a significant proportion of the region.

Since then the climate has become progressively drier, grassland has greatly expanded again and the forests have retreated. So today, forests in East Africa are restricted to regions around the bases of the

15

great mountains in Kenya and Tanzania where rainfall is still high, and to small patches in Uganda such as the Maramagambo and Kibale forests in areas which are wetter throughout the year.

Some of these forest areas have been isolated for many thousands of years, separated like islands by vast tracts of different habitats. Consequently, evolution has continued and you may now find different races or sub-species of animals and plants in some of these montane forest regions.

Much information about the last 4 million years has been gleaned from rich finds of fossils in Kenya and Tanzania. In particular, the meticulous work of Louis and Mary Leakey, carried out over many years at Olduvai and Laetoli, has greatly extended knowledge about this period. It is astonishing how many fossils of extinct species were discovered by the Leakeys, quite apart from those of early hominids which made them famous.

Evidence that hominids had lived at Laetoli 3·5 million years ago came to light when Mary Leakey uncovered their fossilised footsteps. The tracks had been made in soft volcanic ash which had then become dampened by rain and quickly covered by more deposits. They had been made by three individuals, and were identified with the help of fossils of the same period as those of *Australopithecus afarensis*. They walked upright and the tallest was probably about 1·4 m in height. Animal tracks criss-crossed the area including those of an extinct 3-toed horse about a metre high, a close relative of the elephant which had no tusks in the upper jaw, but downwardly- projecting ones in the lower, and other species which were indistinguishable from our modern ones, such as hare, giraffe and guineafowl.

Further important hominid fossils were found by the Leakeys at Olduvai. They belonged to two distinct species, estimated at 1·75 million years old. One of these, *Australopithecus boisei*, the taller of the two, was more heavily built and had teeth adapted to a vegetarian diet. The other, *Homo habilis*, thought to be a direct ancestor of modern man, was more slightly built and had a larger brain. Simple stone tools found in the same deposits indicated that this hominid was a hunter as well as an eater of plant material.

The various strata at Olduvai in which fossils were found consist of successive layers of volcanic ash deposited over the past 1·75 million years. These strata could be accurately dated and were so well defined that it became possible to deduce from their composition and fossil content the major climatic changes that had occurred and the sequence of animal species that had occupied the site over this period. Just before the deposition began, a volcanic eruption had covered the area with laval flows and a large, shallow soda lake had formed there. The hominids lived around the edge of the lake and a great variety of mammals and birds were drawn to the area by the presence of water. Their fossilised remains include those of many antelope species, two kinds of giraffe – one with projecting horns like a deer's antlers – white rhino, two species of elephant and a number of predators such as hyaena, jackal, sabre-toothed cat (so called because of its long stabbing canines) and a fore-runner of the lion we know today. Hippos and crocodiles lived in the lake and cormorants and pelicans fished its waters.

Fossils found in rather later deposits around 1·5 million years ago were more typical of animals inhabiting open savannah; they contained many giant forms. There were huge buffaloes, giant pigs, baboons half as big again as the present species, large rhinos and a great number of antelope including a magnificent species of greater kudu, much larger than the present one. *Australopithecus bosei* was still present, but *Homo habilis* had evolved into *Homo erectus*, a human with a much larger brain who made excellent hand axes and was a hunter-gatherer.

A very dry, hot period followed from which few fossils were recovered, but around 800,000 years ago it became much wetter – lakes and streams formed, and the surrounding savannah became a mosaic of habitat types once more. Around Olduvai, it was never wet enough to form forest, but in many other parts of East Africa, forests expanded considerably. When this happened, some species left the retreating plains and successfully colonised the forest. The bongo, which was once a plains species, was one of these, and it is probable that tree hyrax and certain tree squirrels have also evolved from savannah types. The reverse was true during dry periods when the forests retreated; the klipspringer, for instance, is an antelope which came from forest forebears.

It is probable that the species which were able to make a successful transition either to or from the forest had already become adapted to living around the margins of forest and savannah. Today we also have species which have a foot in both habitats and sometimes switch from one to another according to conditions; these include elephant, buffalo and leopard. Perhaps these too would have a better chance of survival if the climate changed once more.

Half a million years ago the mammalian fauna was basically very similar to what it is today. However, it is not certain when *Homo erectus* became extinct and *Homo sapiens* first appeared. Perhaps more fossil evidence will come to light during future excavations.

So the panorama of species we see today, merely represents a stage in evolutionary history. What further changes occur in the centuries that lie ahead will largely depend on one species, *Homo sapiens*. Human encroachment on wildlife habitats and exploitation of its fauna have already had a profound impact, and the very existence of these remarkable assemblages of plants and animals now depends on economic and political factors. There are great problems to be overcome, but with vision and great determination this precious wildlife heritage may yet be saved for future generations, but it will take much wisdom to steer a satisfactory course between human need and greed.

CHAPTER 2

Living Together

Inter-relationships are the key to understanding what is going on in the living world, so in this chapter the various kinds of relationships will be described, and the basic principles of how animals and plants interact with one another and with their environment, discussed.

Plants and animals do not occur in haphazard collections but live together in communities where their lives are intimately linked. Every different habitat has its characteristic community; in a fast-flowing stream, for example, the animals and plants you find there are very different from those in the lake into which it flows. Even the smallest communities will contain many interacting species. To illustrate the complexities of these inter-relationships, I will take a community based on the umbrella acacia, a tree commonly found on the East African savannah.

The whole tree provides welcome shade for elephant, buffalo and antelopes such as impala, which in return for this facility, cover the ground beneath with their droppings. The droppings eventually decay and provide nutrients which are absorbed by the tree's roots and help its growth. The tree also provides nesting sites for birds, including colonies of weavers which festoon the branches with their hanging nests.

All parts of the tree provide food for animals. The leaves are nibbled by caterpillars and their juices extracted by bugs which use their piercing mouthparts for the purpose; giraffes use their long necks to browse the leaves, rock hyraxes climb for them and elephants will even break off boughs in order to get at them.

The boughs are bored into by beetle grubs which feed on the more nutritious material just below the bark. They sometimes remain in their tunnel systems for several years before eventually emerging as adults. The boughs broken by the elephants expose these tunnels and make it easier for woodpeckers, shrikes and barbets to extract the grubs with their beaks which are well adapted for the purpose.

During the early part of the year the tree produces a mass of tiny, cream coloured pom-pom flowers which are eaten voraciously by vervet monkeys. The flowers also provide nectar for numerous white butterflies and pollen for a host of tiny beetles. These bring about pollination and cause the seeds to set. The profusion of insects in their turn provide food for many insectivorous birds such as warblers and flycatchers which frequent the trees at this time.

When the flowers die and pods form, the vervets again visit the trees to eat the developing seeds; they tear open the pods to extract them, throwing the outer husks to the ground where impala or elephant may make a meal of them.

There is also a species of small beetle which lays its eggs on the surface of young pods, and when the eggs hatch, the grubs bore inside and feed on the developing seeds, just as you sometimes find grubs in a pea pod. By the time the adult beetles emerge, another season will have arrived and the cycle can be repeated. But not all the seeds are destroyed by the beetle grubs, so when the pods become dry and fall to the ground, they provide more food for impala and elephant. Elephant are extremely fond of them, and will shake the tree with their trunks and even break down boughs to get at them. However, not all the seeds eaten are ground up by the teeth and digested, many go right through and pass out with the droppings. During their passage through the elephant's gut, the very hard seed coats become conveniently softened by the digestive juices and this helps germination.

Dung beetles collect some of the dung from beneath the tree, roll it into a ball and trundle it across the grass for long distances. The ball is then buried and a single egg laid on it, and when the grub hatches, the dung provides more than enough food for it to grow into an adult beetle. If an acacia seed happens to be lodged in the dung ball it will germinate during the next rains and get off to a good start, using the nutrients from the remaining dung. Thus acacia seedlings become widely dispersed from the parent tree. What happens to them next depends on many factors. The majority will be eaten as young seedlings, others may survive longer and become sufficiently woody to survive constant nibbling and even fire. It could be 50 years or more before a seedling reaches tree size, having been browsed and burnt many times.

In later chapters some of the inter-relationships between animals, plants and the environment will be described for three main ecosystems – savannah, lakes and forests. These have been chosen because they are the most likely ones for the visitor to encounter during a safari. But first it would be helpful to discuss in more detail the characteristics of an ecosystem, as these provide the broad canvas on which the staggering variety of species is painted to produce a complete picture.

Ecosystems are large inter-related units consisting of many communities of plants and animals plus the environment in which they live. A forest ecosystem, for example, is not uniform and may contain communities of many kinds. Each species of tree within the forest has a number of animal species associated with it, the soil has an entirely different community and so does the leaf litter on the forest floor; boggy places in the forest have their own communities, waterholes in forest clearings, rather different ones – the list could go on and on, but all are part of the forest ecosystem.

All sorts of factors determine the nature of an ecosystem. The non-living ones include climate (particularly rainfall, temperature and light), the kind of soil and its water content, and such physiographic factors as altitude and slope. All these interact with one another to determine the type of vegetation that is able to grow there. In addition, the animals and plants, not only interact with each other, but with the environment as well, and the environment interacts with them.

If you climb Kilimanjaro the dramatic influence of altitude, rainfall and temperature becomes obvious as you pass through different levels of vegetation. Near the base of the mountain, high rainfall allows tropical rain forest to flourish. This is largely composed of tall broad-leaved trees, but nearer the upper limits of this zone you pass through rather different forest which includes such species as *Podocarpus*, a rather primitive conifer with leaves like those of a yew, giant tree heathers, tall bushy *Hypericum* with large yellow flowers and immense specimens of camphor-wood emerging high above the rest. Then, with dramatic suddenness at around 2800 m, you leave the trees behind and the countryside opens out into heathland, dominated by heathers and heath-like shrubs with clumps of everlasting flowers.

21

A main cause of vegetational changes as you leave the forest and journey towards the summit, is the progressive reduction in rainfall. As you climb steadily upwards through the heathland, the heathers soon disappear and tussocky grasses begin to dominate. You are now in the moorland zone with its strange giant senecios and tall lobelias. Around 4500 m you come to highland desert which is typical of the saddle region which spans the two main peaks. Here, conditions are harsh, with temperatures around freezing at night and up to 40°C by day, rainfall is slight and there are sometimes extremely high winds; only the hardiest of plants can survive here. You then reach a region completely devoid of vegetation which looks more like a moonscape. There are scattered bare boulders, and the ground surface is of shifting pumice which makes life extremely trying for the climber. Then comes the snow. By this time you have made a journey through zones of vegetation resembling in many ways those seen when travelling from the equator to the arctic, but this time it is up-hill most of the way!

Ecosystems are to a large extent inter-dependent units, although their boundaries are seldom rigid. As we saw with the zones on Kili-manjaro, sometimes they merge gradually into one another, at other times the boundary is more strictly defined. But with animals such as insects, birds and mammals which have good means of locomotion there is inevitably some interchange between ecosystems.

In every ecosystem there is a similar basic plan, which is based on feeding relationships; it has been likened to a pyramid of life forms. This pyramid is made up of well-defined steps between base and apex, each representing a group of organisms with a similar means of nutrition. There are three main types, the producers of food, the consumers of that food and the decomposers which recycle it.

The base of the pyramid represents the green plants – the food producers. Green plants are the only organisms capable of harnessing the energy of the sun directly. They do this when they photosynthesise. As a result of this process they build up sugars and starches, and with the help of nutrients in the soil make proteins as well. This food is used by green plants for their own growth and energy requirements and in addition, provides all other living organisms with the food and energy they need. This happens directly when the plants are eaten by animals, or indirectly through an intermediate step in the food chain.

The productivity of an ecosystem, i.e. the fresh or live weight (biomass) of plant material produced over a given period of time varies enormously according to the type of vegetation present. In savannah, productivity is very high due to the abundance of nutritious grasses;

in lakes the key to productivity is the quantity of microscopic algae in the water, and in forests it is the trees that are the main producers of food.

The next step up the pyramid represents the large numbers of plant-eaters (herbivores) present in the ecosystem. These are the first of the consumers which obtain the substances they need for growth and energy by feeding directly on green plants. Herbivores come in all shapes and sizes: aphids, caterpillars, snails, antelopes, colobus monkeys and elephants, to name just a few.

The third step represents the carnivores which feed on animal tissues and so get the sun's energy via the vegetarians which obtained it from the green plants. This group not only contains the flesh-eating mammals and birds such as lions and eagles, but also a host of insect-eating species and those which feed on earthworms and molluscs. So a warbler feeding on a caterpillar is as much a carnivore as a leopard feeding on an antelope.

In some communities there may be further steps in the pyramid when larger carnivores feed on smaller ones. In some large lakes, crocodiles eat large carnivorous fish which in turn take smaller fish which depend on plant plankton for their food. Also, in the savannah there are eagles which eat snakes, which feed on lizards, which take grasshoppers which feed on grass.

However, not all animals die by being killed and eaten; many succumb in other ways, and their remains, along with the waste products of living animals and plants, become the food of another group which contains the scavengers and decomposers. These include animals such as termites and earthworms which feed on dead plant material; those which feed on carrion, such as vultures and marabou storks; and feeders on dung which include maggots and dung beetles. Then, when they have done their bit, it is the turn of the true decomposers, fungi and bacteria, to bring about the decay of any material remaining, converting it into carbon dioxide, water and nutrients. These simple substances are then available once more to the green plants, and the cycle starts all over again.

Thus an ecosystem is self-perpetuating with energy constantly passing through its food web, and material being recycled over and over again. This does not mean that an ecosystem never changes. In the short term, fluctuations are occurring all the time due to many factors, but although links may weaken or strengthen, the basic structure survives. However, over longer periods, changes in climate, volcanic action, fire and such like may alter the nature of an ecosystem completely, as when lakes dry up and turn into grassland, and grassland becomes forest. Man too, can change an ecosystem when he cuts down a rain forest or dams a river.

There is an interesting numerical relationship between the organisms in the various steps of the pyramid. To take a simple example, it has been calculated that over a year, about 2.5 km^2 of grass is needed to support 100 gazelles, which in turn are needed for the survival of a single lion. This represents a significant loss of material at each step, due to the fact that much of the food eaten by an animal remains undigested and passes out as waste, and some is broken down in respiration to supply energy for the animal's own use. Many animals convert no more than 10% of their food into body tissue, some herbivores even less. So in the following food chain (in which the arrows represent the direction of flow of energy through it)

$$\text{plant plankton} \rightarrow \text{tilapia fish} \rightarrow \text{tiger fish} \rightarrow \text{crocodile}$$

1000 kg of plant plankton would be needed to produce 100 kg of tilapia to form 10 kg of tiger fish to produce 1 kg of crocodile tissue. There is a comparable loss of energy to the atmosphere in the form of heat, so it follows that the fewer the steps in the food chain the more energy will be available for the species at the top.

Every species within an ecosystem has its own niche for which it is uniquely fitted. The term niche, not only denotes the animal's position in the food web and what it eats, but also its way of life. For example, in a forest there are several niches for animals which feed on leaves: there are insects which use a proboscis to suck out the leaf's juices, caterpillars which bite off pieces of the leaves, forest antelopes which take whole leaves within reach of the ground and monkeys that can climb to obtain leaves higher up. All these animals feed on leaves, but each is adapted in a different way for utilising the resource, so it occupies a different niche. When various ecosystems are discussed in later chapters it will become evident that the many species present are able to share out the available resources because each has its special niche. In this way, competition for the available food is greatly reduced.

Animals occupying different niches show varying degrees of flexibility. Some species, like giraffes, cheetahs and woodpeckers are specialists, being dependent on very few kinds of food which they exploit using highly specialised structures and techniques. Others such as elephant, baboon and leopard are generalists which depend on a much greater range of food items, are able to adapt more easily when changes occur and are more opportunistic when feeding.

Whatever the niche, each animal needs to satisfy life's three basic requirements: to obtain enough food to survive, to breed so that its genes are passed on to the next generation, and to protect itself so that it does not end up prematurely in another animal's stomach. Every species is beautifully adapted in structure, physiology and behaviour to fulfil these requirements. For example, the legs of an antelope, a frog and a praying mantis are very different, each has evolved into a specialised tool for a particular job. Again, these three animals live in very different environments and feed on quite different food, so their physiology has to be suitably adjusted to the conditions they encounter and the food they eat. But structural and physiological adaptations on their own are not enough; it is vital that the animal behaves in the appropriate manner to bring about the required result. When you are watching animals, their structural adaptations are of great interest, but it is their behaviour that transforms them into such marvelously intriguing creatures. These adaptations will be a constant theme in the chapters that follow.

Inter-relationships within an ecosystem may be between members of the same species or between different ones. The former include those special relationships between mother and young, males with males, males with females and females with other females. These relationships become particularly important when animals live in social groups, such as zebra families, hyaena clans and lion prides.

By living together in a society, individuals increase their chances of survival, but for a society to be successful relationships need to be governed by rules. In some social groups, one male has dominant status over other males regarding reproductive rights, as in dwarf mongooses; in others, there may be a dominant female which is the main breeder, as in hunting dogs. Because individuals within a social group vary in size, age and fitness a hierarchy or 'peck order' often develops where each knows its place in the system; once established, this lessens aggression between members of the group. Such a system ensures that in times of hardship the strongest members are more likely to survive. When watching groups of animals it is fascinating to see this constant interaction between its members and try to puzzle out what is going on.

We have already had many examples of food-relationships between different species in an ecosystem, but some of special significance need describing in greater detail.

Predator and prey

Predators and their prey have evolved together, each reacting to the advances of the other as in an arms race. Thus the herbivores of the savannah have greatly benefited when predators have weeded out the slower, the diseased, the more naive and the less alert, allowing the genes of the fittest to be passed on from generation to generation. In this way the stock has been improved and the characteristics with survival value, enhanced. This process continues today.

You can see this selection happening when predators such as hyaenas or hunting dogs run into a herd of gnus (wildebeest) to disturb them. By so doing it makes it easier for them to spot any individual which shows signs of being more vulnerable to attack.

It is not easy to tell how predators affect prey numbers as most of the evidence is circumstantial; the effect certainly varies considerably according to species. In recent years several antelope species have greatly increased in numbers, but the reedbuck is an obvious exception. Reedbuck tend to occur in habitats where leopard and lion are frequent, and here in all probability, the predators have a marked effect. This seems likely, as in places where these predators are scarce, reedbuck numbers are greater. Such a place is around Lake Nakuru, where predator pressure is light, there being no lion, and the relatively few leopard present rely more on the abundant waterbuck.

Thomson's gazelles, the prey of so many species, may also have their numbers controlled in this way in spite of bearing young twice a year, which to some extent compensates for their losses. It may also be true that hunting dogs control impala populations, as in some places where hunting dogs have been ruthlessly destroyed and others where distemper has caused their near extinction, the number of impala has greatly increased.

However, predators certainly exert sufficient pressure to prevent a population explosion in many prey species. By holding numbers below the maximum which the habitat can support, they reduce the effect of starvation and disease which inevitably follow when populations explode. It is when people interfere by culling the predators that big problems may arise. Predators are often better wildlife managers than humans.

Parasites and their hosts

Parasitism is just another mode of life, comparable to being a predator or a herbivore, but its distinguishing feature is that a parasite feeds on living tissues, and to do this, lives within or on the surface of the body of another living organism. All the larger animals and plants have their parasites, but the visitor on safari is unlikely to encounter many species, apart from a few ticks which treat him or her as a potential host when walking through grass which has previously been grazed by herbivores.

The parasitic niche within an ecosystem is an intriguing one, as a parasite's adaptations are often complex and sophisticated. Not only do they have to adapt to living on or in a host which uses all sorts of devices to remove them, but when they reproduce there has to be a means of getting the progeny to another host. This is usually so chancy that they have to lay vast numbers of eggs to reduce the odds. The host is also well adapted for counteracting any harmful effects of the parasite, so a sort of equilibrium is reached between parasite numbers and the host's resistance. It is usually when the host is weak or diseased that large numbers build up and their effect is severe. However, it is surprising what a vast number of roundworms, for example, can exist in the gut of some herbivores without doing any obvious harm.

To illustrate the mode of life of a parasite we will consider one of the common ticks. Ticks are surface parasites, related to mites and spiders. They suck the blood of their hosts and are completely dependent on them. They can be very numerous on the skins of such herbivores as rhinos, buffaloes, warthogs and the larger antelopes. One researcher counted 2,000 on the legs and one side of a water-buck's body.

Ticks are notoriously difficult to dislodge when their mouthparts are deeply embedded in the skin. Elephants do their best to remove them by having a mud bath, and when the mud has dried hard around the parasites, they rub their sides vigorously against a tree trunk or termite mound to crush and rub them off with the mud.

When ticks are mature and gorged with blood, they mate, drop off their host, lay their eggs and die. The eggs hatch into larvae which climb to the top of grass stems and wait for a passing mammal. On being brushed against, they grasp the animal's hairs and waste no time in attaching themselves firmly to the skin with their mandibles. Some species moult several times while on the host, others drop off after every moult and have to climb grass stems on each occasion to await another victim. Ticks exemplify the ultimate in patience, as an adult can go without a meal for several years, waiting for something to turn up.

Many internal parasites cause diseases which may have much more serious effects on the host than surface parasites. These include the trypanosomes which are carried from one host to another by the tsetse fly. Warthogs and various species of antelopes are among those which are affected, but on the whole the wild mammals are largely immune from serious consequences. Only when a tsetse carries the parasites to domestic cattle does the disease, nagana, occur, often with fatal results. Sleeping sickness in humans is caused in the same manner. One disease of great importance to wildlife is rinderpest. This highly contagious disease is caused by a virus. Gnus are very susceptible to attack, and at times their numbers have been greatly reduced by epidemics of this disease.

Symbiosis

This kind of inter-relationship occurs when species associate together for mutual advantage. One example which every visitor to a national park will notice, is that between herbivores and oxpeckers. These remarkable birds, allied to starlings, feed mainly on ticks and other surface parasites and associate with herbivores for almost the whole of their lives. A herd of buffalo, for example, can provide enough parasites to satisfy a flock of oxpeckers on a permanent basis. It is fascinating to see these birds running about the host's body, eagerly prying into creases in the skin and investigating ears and nostrils for parasites. They may also visit open sores to feed on blood, damaged tissue and any flies that have gathered; they also pick off blood-sucking flies which are biting their hosts. Oxpeckers are wonderfully adapted for their specialised mode of life, having sharp-clawed feet for clinging in any position to the host's skin, a stiff tail like a woodpecker's for extra support and a laterally-flattened bill for prising up the ticks which are fastened tightly to the skin. When dusk comes, the birds fly off to their roosting places, but they are back again when dawn breaks.

This relationship is by no means one-sided as the herbivores benefit from having their parasites removed, and when disturbed, the birds fly up making loud alarm calls which alert the animals to possible danger. Rhinos take particular notice of this warning, partly no doubt because their eyesight is very poor.

When watching crocodiles basking on a sand bank, you may see common sandpipers or plovers associating with them. The crocodiles benefit from these birds' attention as they remove parasites from between their scales and even take leeches from their open mouths. When the birds are disturbed, they fly off making loud discordant noises which alert the crocodiles to possible danger, giving them time to slip into the water. The birds in their turn benefit by getting extra food when they groom the crocodiles, and quite often by choosing a nest site quite near to a regular basking place. Potential egg thieves would think twice before venturing too near the crocodiles.

Another symbiotic relationship occurs between guineafowl and several species of smaller birds. You see this happening in early morning or late afternoon when guineafowl are busily feeding. While searching for insects and seeds, they vigorously scratch the dusty soil, like hens in a farmyard, and this attracts birds such as starlings and buffalo weavers which pick up anything missed by the guineafowl. The smaller birds are probably more alert than the guineafowl, which appear to be concentrating more on the search for food. So in return for the extra food they find in this way, the guineafowl get early warning of danger when the smaller birds fly up, making their shrill alarm calls.

Symbiosis can also occur between animals and plants. One remarkable relationship of this kind is between ants and the whistling thorn, *Acacia drepanolobium*. It is not long before you see whistling thorn when travelling through Kenya. The species covers large areas of Nairobi National Park, and when travelling across the Rift on the way to the Mara it becomes the dominant shrub as you near the Mau Escarpment; it is common in many other regions too. Recognition is easy as these shrubby trees bear prolific black galls and long white spines. Each gall has a number of small holes on its surface, and the name, whistling thorn, refers to the noise the wind makes when it passes through the myriads of galls. If you tap a gall smartly, an ant is likely to pop out of one of the holes; others will follow and rush about in an agitated manner. The ants are very aggressive and will attack the muzzle of any browser, such as a giraffe, biting it with powerful mandibles. The attack causes the giraffe to restrict its feeding to short periods before moving to another part of the bush, and thus prevents excessive damage to the vegetation. The protection given by the ants to the acacia is undoubtedly a useful addition to the armoury of spines, and the relationship is also beneficial to the ants as they are supplied with tough shelters, guarded by spines, and sugar secretions from the acacia provide extra food on their doorstep.

So when you visit an ecosystem such as savannah you are viewing the product of an infinitely complex and varied web of inter-relationships between plants, animals and the non-living environment. This leads one to the philosophical concept that all life is, in reality, about relationships.

CHAPTER 3

Savannah: Vegetation and Herbivores

Savannah is basically grassland, but it varies greatly according to the vegetation, particularly the presence of trees. It is useful to distinguish three types, although they do tend to merge into one another. First there are the short grass plains which typify the southern and eastern parts of the Serengeti, where you hardly see a tree for many kilometres. Second there is woody savannah where trees, particularly acacias, relieve the monotony of the grassy plains. Third, there is bushy savannah where there are more bushes than trees, but with large areas of grass between. Savannah merges into true woodland when the trees become thick and their shade covers more than 20% of the land.

Various factors, such as type of soil, temperature, rainfall and topography cause these differences, and within the savannah, rivers, which are often seasonal, provide local variations in vegetation, such as lines of yellow-barked acacias, riverine bush or even riverine forest.

Grass can thrive in a climate where wet and dry seasons are pronounced and rainfall is between 500–750 mm in most years. Occasional thunder showers during the dry season are an added bonus. There are many species of grass, but it is useful to divide them into the annuals which grow fast, form abundant seeds and die in one short season, and the perennials which have some means of surviving the long periods of drought. The perennials all have fibrous roots which can penetrate deeply if soil conditions allow, and some have rhizomes or runners in which food is stored. Some grasses are tussocky, others when mature look like a cereal crop, while others have a creeping habit and form mats.

Fire, both natural and contrived, is a real threat to vegetation in the dry season, but grasses manage very well in spite of having all surface growth destroyed, as their underground portions remain alive and readily sprout once more when the rains return.

Grasses can also cope with the trampling and grazing of large herbivores. Unlike many plants, growth occurs in grass leaves, mainly at the base, so when most of the leaf is eaten, the remainder continues to grow. What is more, the saliva left on the cut surfaces by the grazer contains a substance that stimulates growth. The savannah has been usefully likened to a lawn which is cut, rolled and periodically pronged and thus aerated; instead it is grazed, trampled and cut by hooves. As with lawns, there are other plants which grow among the grasses, including many species allied to clovers which fix nitrogen from the atmosphere. These nutritious plants are useful additions to an otherwise monotonous diet of grass and are particularly sought after by some species of herbivore.

The herbivores

Grasses and herbivores have evolved together, each reacting to the advances of the other. This has resulted in a magnificent spectacle of herbivore evolution which probably reached its peak some 10–15 million years ago, although many refinements have occurred during the past two million years, due partly to the drier climate which caused the retreat of the forests and the spread of grasslands. Over the millennia the grasses responded to herbivore pressure and drier conditions by becoming coarser, more fibrous and in some cases siliceous. These changes caused the grinding teeth of the grazers to wear down more quickly, so over the years the teeth responded by becoming more efficient grinders. They became larger and closer together, their surfaces, flatter and ridged, and growth continued throughout life, thus compensating for wear.

Another important evolutionary step was to exploit the advantages of chewing the cud. This is characteristic of the family Bovidae, which includes the buffaloes and antelopes. Chewing the cud is useful because it increases the efficiency of digestion of cellulose and related substances, and it can occur during rest periods between bouts of grazing or browsing, and in places of greater safety.

Bovids have a four-chambered stomach. When the grass is mixed with saliva, chewed and swallowed, it passes into the first chamber. Here there are astronomical numbers of bacteria and protozoa which together ferment the plant material which the animal's digestive juices are unable to cope with. This is an example of symbiosis between micro-organisms and the ruminant. Both benefit, as the former live in a protected habitat and have their food conveniently delivered, while the latter reaps the benefit of a more efficient digestive process.

The cud is regurgitated into the mouth for further pulverisation before being swallowed once more. This can happen repeatedly, until the products are fine enough to pass into the second chamber where the brew continues to ferment. After some time the products pass into the third and fourth chambers which correspond approximately to the true stomach of other mammals. Here, hydrochloric acid and enzymes are secreted which start the digestion of protein. The products then pass into the duodenum where digestion is completed and the soluble substances can be absorbed.

The evolution of larger size and longer legs has probably arisen in relation to both food and predator pressure, although as a spin-off these have also been very useful for coping with fire. Longer legs and stronger bodies enable a herbivore to reach new pastures more quickly. This is a great advantage where over-grazing by large herds occurs and when isolated storms cause rain to fall over local areas, stimulating the growth of grass in those places. Longer legs also enhance the chances of avoiding predators, and the evolution of hooves adds to the animal's speed and manoeuvrability, just as running shoes help athletes.

The shape of an antelope is also a consequence of evolutionary pressures. As the legs increased in length as a response to predators the head became further away from the food, so natural selection favoured variations allowing increase in neck length. The sense organs also became more acute. The snout elongated, and internally the surface area of the sensory membranes of the olfactory organs increased enormously, allowing the detection of incredibly low concentrations of scents. The development of large ears, capable of independent movement, enabled the owner to pin-point the direction of any sound; and the formation of large bulging eyes, projecting from the sides of the head allowed it to increase its field of view to nearly 360°. In addition, with the muzzle near the ground for so much of the time when feeding, touch organs on the lips became more numerous.

These factors may help to explain why so many species of antelope look rather similar.

Why so much diversity of species on the savannah?

Productivity in savannah is very high so there is plenty of food available for a host of herbivores, but the supply is seasonal and too much competition for resources could lead to disaster. Thus in the course of evolution competition between many species has been minimised by making each a specialist feeder, beautifully adapted to take its particular share of the bounty. Of course there is overlap, but the system is superb with each species occupying its unique niche in the ecosystem. There are many ways in which this reduction in competition is achieved.

The first means of separation is through choice of habitat. Savannah varies greatly from one area to another. So you find zebras, gnus and gazelles on the open plains, kudus, bushbuck and dikdik in more woody or bushy areas and waterbuck and reedbuck in riverine or marshy habitats.

There are also physiological reasons for such separations, particularly in the need for drinking water. Those which have to drink every day can only live in regions near the source of supply, so here we may find waterbuck, reedbuck and buffalo. Others can manage with less if circumstances demand, for example, gnus and zebras can go without water for two or three days. Oryx go one better and can abstain for weeks at a time, although they do occasionally drink when water is easily available. Grant's gazelles can go without drinking altogether, relying only on the water in the vegetation and dew that may form at night.

Competition is also reduced when different species select different kinds of food. In broad terms you find that some, such as gazelles, gnus and zebras are exclusively grazers, others, including giraffe, bushbuck and black rhino, are browsers, and some are more flexible, making the best of both worlds by grazing or browsing according to availability. The latter, which contains elephant and impala, are therefore capable of exploiting a greater variety of habitats.

Within these broad categories you find that species have their own specialised requirements for which they are well adapted in structure and behaviour. This is well illustrated by what is known as the 'grazing succession', which applies particularly to the long grass plains of the Mara and Serengeti. Long grass is avoided by the smaller herbivores as they cannot find quality grasses there and it may also conceal predators, but elephants can utilise coarser material and having nothing to fear, they are usually the first to exploit such an area. Buffaloes often follow the elephants, and much more trampling takes place. If conditions are damp enough, the trampled grass will sprout new nutritious shoots which attract gnus and zebras, and these are followed by gazelles and kongoni (hartebeest) which pluck the scattered broad-leaved plants and the individual grass shoots left by the others – their pointed muzzles are well adapted for such selection.

Zebra and gnu are often seen grazing together, but they too have their preferences. Zebras are more tolerant of coarse grasses, having incisor teeth in both jaws which can easily nip off the tough stems. Gnus with their broader mouths prefer the leafier parts of the grasses, mowing them down with the help of their front spatulate teeth which bite against a relatively soft pad on the upper. This device reduces tooth wear.

Eland are more specialised feeders choosing the more nutritious leguminous and other broad-leaved plants. These have to be searched for as they are less numerous than the grasses, so eland tend to be in small groups and are found only where their food is in reasonable quantities. Because their food is so nutritious, a larger sized body has become possible.

Browsers show a comparable specialisation for reducing competition for the available food, browsing at certain heights according to their reach and build. A giraffe's remarkable neck allows it to feed on nutritious tufts of acacia leaves up to 6 m, well out of reach of any other competitors on the ground. In many parks where giraffe are numerous, this browsing produces an hour-glass effect on the trees, the top expansion being the part the animals cannot reach.

In more scrubby areas, such as Samburu, Tsavo and parts of Amboseli you are likely to see gerenuk. These graceful, long-necked antelopes browse below the levels giraffe prefer. In addition to using their long necks, they regularly rise on their hind legs using their front ones to support themselves against the bush and also to manipulate branches to bring the leaves within easier reach.

Bushbuck browse at a still lower level in the same bushy habitat, but choose to feed more in the late evening or at night, while black rhino, although bulky, have short necks and prefer to browse a few feet from the ground, a favourite habitat being grassy plains dotted with short acacia bushes. Then there is the dikdik which uses its diminutive proportions to penetrate bushes and feed on the low browse other species cannot reach.

The ability to migrate is a further feeding adaptation which allows a species to exploit a habitat according to season. Gnu, zebra and the gazelles all carry out considerable migrations, particularly in the Serengeti. Here, migration becomes necessary because the short-grass plains in south-eastern Serengeti have no permanent water, but in the rainy season they provide short, sweet, nutritious grass, ideal for grazing during the breeding season. But by the end of May or beginning of June, what is left of the grasses becomes dry, and the herds move west and north to more wooded areas where permanent water is to be found. Visitors to the short-grass plains during the dry season may be disappointed to see mile after mile of scorched, brown, dusty savannah, flat as a pancake and with hardly an animal in sight. By contrast, between November and May, the same area may be crowded with a million or more gnu, zebra and gazelle, a truly breath-taking spectacle. But if you do come in the dry season, take heart, you will find the great herds elsewhere.

The general movement west and north from late May onwards is often a gradual one. In June and early July the herds will most likely be in the wooded areas around Seronera, in the 'corridor' and on the plains in the north of the park. By late July and through to September great concentrations will have reached the Maasai Mara in Kenya and beyond the park boundaries. By late October or early November they are drifting back, and with a few good thunderstorms to encourage them, there may be many thousands around Seronera and Banagi. Predictions about the whereabouts of the herds are always risky as rainstorms often cause to and fro movements and no two seasons are alike. However, by the end of November they should be back on the short-grass plains which are by then lush again after the rains. By that time many of the animals will have completed a round trip of over 800 km.

The period of the rut for gnu coincides with the outward migration from the short-grass plains in April or May. This is a time of great activity, with territorial males fighting for mating rights over groups of females. Rivers are crossed, often with heavy losses, but relentlessly the herds progress, spurred on by an instinct to find new pastures and water. The calves are born when back again on the short-grass plains, the great majority during a three-week period from the end of January. In the Ngorongoro Crater, Amboseli and a few other areas the gnus have no need to migrate as water is always available, so even in the dry season the visitor can see them there.

Burchell's zebra also migrate in large numbers, usually preceding the gnus. Their collective movements through the long grass help to expose the green portions preferred by the gnus that follow. In the Serengeti, Thomson's gazelles also migrate, but their journeyings are not so extensive as the others. By June, very few herbivores remain on the short-grass plains apart from a few Grant's gazelles which stay on their scorched and desolate territories until the rains bring the herds back again.

Adaptations of herbivores to predation

There are few hiding places on the open plains although some species, such as warthog and spring-hare, dig burrows. The territory of a warthog family may hold several of these refuges which have entrances just large enough for a warthog, but too small for the larger predators to enter unless an attempt is made to dig the prey out. If it has time, when fleeing for safety, a warthog will enter its burrow backwards, so the predator is faced with its formidable tusks. However, a hungry lion will sometimes succeed in killing a warthog even when it is in its burrow.

Spring-hares also live during the day in burrow systems. These large, nocturnal, herbivorous rodents have greatly elongated hind legs, and if disturbed in the open, leap about like miniature kangaroos as they head for the safety of their burrows.

For most herbivores living on the plains, running is the usual method of avoiding predators, and this can be made more effective by special behavioural strategies. A Thomson's gazelle, for example, when chased by a predator will keep tabs on the exact position of its pursuer by zig-zag running. This enables it to see immediately behind it – a blind spot when running straight. Another device is used by a herd of zebra when attacked by lion; the animals seem to explode in all directions. It is possible that their pattern of stripes adds to the confusion and prevents the predator from concentrating on a single animal. Impala carry out a similar manoeuvre, making prodigious leaps to escape from attack.

Keeping alert is the key to survival, and one of the major hazards faced by a herbivore is having to go to water at intervals in order to drink. It is always interesting to watch a herd of zebra come to water in the heat of the day. They approach very tentatively, and rightly so, as a rush to the water might well be fatal. Predators often lie in wait near water holes. As a few animals venture nearer, the others just stand and watch ready to bound away at the first sign of danger, real or imagined. There is no hurry; eyes, ears and nostrils are all on red alert for the slightest sign, and only when sufficiently assured will a few start to drink. But all the time others keep watch, waiting their turn at the water's edge when the first have slaked their thirst. This pattern of alertness is also seen when herds are grazing; not all have their heads down at the same time, and when resting out on the plains, one animal may lean its neck on another so that their combined field of view covers 360°.

When on migration, gnus move head to tail in long lines, sometimes miles long. This linear formation lessens the chance of stumbling on concealed lions; moving on a broad front would be much more hazardous. When on a walking safari, a similar formation is adopted by people for safety reasons. The effect of gnu movements on the savannah becomes strikingly evident in the form of well-defined narrow trails, worn by the impact of thousands of feet.

Reproductive strategies to avoid predation

The reproductive season is the time when herbivores are most vulnerable. Animals in late pregnancy are not so speedy and the calves when born are easy prey. So it is not surprising that various strategies have been devised to counteract predator pressure.

Gnus, by reducing the calving season to a few short weeks ensure that a reasonable number survive, as all the predators become so satiated that many are left. If births were scattered throughout the year a much higher proportion would be killed as young calves are so vulnerable and predators would be more eager to kill. A further device is the speed at which calves become mobile after birth. Young gnus can stand within seven minutes and many other antelopes, including eland and waterbuck, can do so within an hour.

You have a good chance of seeing the birth of a gnu if you are at Amboseli, the Ngorongoro Crater or on the short-grass plains of the Serengeti in early February – the peak of the breeding season. It is well worthwhile spending 20 minutes or so watching a herd as so many calves are being born each day, particularly in the morning. Births also occur at mid-day – a safer time, as then the predators are resting. Focus your attention on any female that lies down, as this often happens just prior to birth. It is a moving sight to see the calf born, encased in the birth membranes, the mother turning round to smell the new arrival and removing the membranes as she licks it clean. Licking and scenting are important as they cement the mother/calf bond and ensure recognition. Then you see the first unco-ordinated struggles as the calf tries to get to its feet, and its first tentative steps as it follows its mother.

37

Gnus, like topi calves, are said to be 'followers' as they follow their mother at once, but the majority of antelopes are 'hiders'. This means that just before birth, the females leave the others and choose some thicket which should screen them from predators. After birth, the calf is abandoned and relies only on its camouflage, its instinct to keep still and the vegetation in which it is lying. The mother visits the calf periodically to suckle, and usually grazes, apparently unconcerned, some distance from where the calf lies hidden. Young Thomson's gazelles may be born right out on the plains. They are parked some distance from each other and lie well camouflaged in the grass. By being randomly dispersed, it is only bad luck if they are discovered by predators.

The variety of social strategies used by herbivores

Herbivores have evolved a number of social strategies which help in their struggle for survival. Some species are solitary for most of their lives, others live in families or adopt the harem principle, while others live in great herds. Within these social groups, different techniques have evolved for carrying out such vital functions as feeding, defence against predators, mating and bringing up the young. Four species will be described which illustrate some of the strategies used.

Loners e.g. black rhino

Black rhinos are essentially solitary, although when they were common it was sometimes possible to see four or five together. The most enduring bond is between mother and calf which may remain together for up to four years.

Although not territorial in the sense of defending an area, they do occupy home ranges, but will tolerate the presence of others in the vicinity; however, interactions do occur. These may sometimes be witnessed after dark at Treetops, Mountain Lodge or The Ark when one rhino is busy at a saltlick and another comes too near. There may be mock charges with upward jerks of the head and horn, accompanied by much huffing and snorting. Fights between rival males over a female in oestrus may be much more serious.

Rhinos defaecate at particular places in their home range, scraping their back feet like a dog to spread the dung. As several rhinos may use the same area for this purpose it seems likely that this ritual conveys information. It is possible that the scent of the dung carried on the feet indicates to others the route a rhino has taken, and it is likely that recognition of individuals can be made through the scent of the dung.

A single calf is born, usually well hidden in thick vegetation. When very young, the calf will follow its mother closely, but after a few weeks, may venture further and do some tentative browsing nearby. The mother will vigorously defend it from attack by lion and may even succeed in killing the predator by repeatedly butting it with her long horn.

An adult rhino is not fully grown until six or seven years old, by which time it could weigh about two tonnes; however, they become mature well before that. There is a complex period of courtship. The male cautiously follows the female, and when she stops, he approaches with a stiff-legged gait. There is usually much to-ing and fro-ing before they face each other, jousting tentatively with their horns. These preliminaries may go on for a long time before mounting eventually takes place. Coition is not achieved at once, and he may mount her many times in the course of perhaps half an hour before mating is successful. A female usually has a calf every four years.

A rhino's daily routine is fairly predictable. Most browsing takes place in the morning, but when the day gets hot, it lies down and perhaps sleeps. Surprisingly, it usually rests in the open, relying on its thick skin to keep out some of the heat. In the late afternoon it becomes active again, and if there is enough water, may spend a few hours half submerged in its welcome coolness. Alternatively, it may indulge in the luxury of a mud wallow to reduce its temperature. After drinking, it will wander slowly back to its feeding grounds and remain active for most of the following night.

It is thought that in some very arid areas rhinos can exist without drinking, relying only on the water in the vegetation consumed. When they browse, they use their prehensile upper lip to help pluck the leaves. They are very selective over the species chosen and usually only their more nutritious portions are eaten.

Rhinos are short-sighted and noted for their aggression, but those seen when on safari are quite used to mini-buses and are usually docile. Those not accustomed to visitors and others, perhaps with experience of poachers, when disturbed by the oxpeckers' alarm calls, may charge with great determination. Usually they stop just short, but sometimes they vent their wrath on the vehicle with spectacular results. A two tonne rhino charging at 50 k.p.h. is a formidable proposition.

Today the black rhino is an endangered species. Poaching has caused its extinction in many areas and reduced the population to critical levels in others. Schemes are currently being carried out to breed them in specially protected areas for later release in those parks where they are relatively more safe. But the position is very serious, and sadly the future of the rhino remains in doubt. It would be tragic if this ancient species, whose ancestry can be traced back more than 25 million years, were to disappear from the face of the earth just because it possessed horns. These formidable structures, made of consolidated hair, are status symbols when used as dagger handles in some middle-eastern countries, and in Eastern Asia are misguidedly considered to have aphrodisiac properties. Fashion and myth have already caused the near extinction of birds and mammals in the past; will history be repeated for the black rhino?

The family e.g. common or Burchell's zebra

Zebra herds are made up of family groups with strong bonds between its members. Each group consists of a single stallion and between 1–6 mares and their foals; on average about 7 animals in all. This differs from the harem of other species where the females are actively herded by the male and constant vigilance has to be kept to see that they do not stray. There may also be bachelor groups composed of young male zebras with older animals no longer in charge of a family group.

When the family moves towards water or on to new pastures the dominant mare leads the way, followed in line by the other mares in a definite order of hierarchy. Any mare which attempts to change her place is threatened by the mare in front which lowers her head and lays back her ears. This gesture is usually sufficient to prevent aggression, fights between mares being rare. When the foals are young, they closely follow their mothers in the line, while the stallion may bring up the rear or trot alongside the group.

Family bonds are strengthened by much mutual grooming between different members of the group, particularly between mare and foal and stallion with mares. The animals face each other and nibble the other's head, neck or back. In so doing they remove loose hair and perhaps rid the other of surface parasites. Grooming may go on for up to half an hour.

Members of a family recognise each other by sight, voice and smell. All zebra patterns are different, so recognition by sight is not difficult. Vocal recognition is more important by night, and has been described as a cross between a bark and a bray. Recognition by scent, as when a colt is seeking out its mother, is initiated when they nose each other.

The stallion is the guardian of the family. He stands by when a mare is giving birth and plays a prominent part if the family is disturbed by predators. When the group runs, he will often lag behind and attack such predators as hyaenas or hunting dogs with flailing hooves. This apparent altruism may occasionally lead to his death, but the remainder of the group escape.

Foals usually leave the family when between 1 and 3 years old. The males are not forced out, but leave of their own accord when their own mother has another foal. However, the females are usually abducted from the family group at the time of their first oestrus. At this time a number of stallions may be attracted, and fights ensue between them and the group stallion. Often the latter's exhaustion, after repelling several others, allows the young mare to be taken from its family. This device helps to prevent in-breeding.

When stallions fight, they try to bite each other's face, neck and legs, rearing on to their hind limbs as they do so. They also kick strongly with their hind legs, especially when being chased.

A mare comes into oestrus a few days after giving birth, and is capable of having a foal every year from the time she is three. She may live 20 years or more.

The evolution of such a strong family unit has been a most successful one, the strong bonds between its members often leading to co-operation or assistance to a weakened member. Under these circumstances the chances of the young surviving are greatly enhanced.

The harem e.g. impala

Impala are probably the most successful medium-sized antelopes in East Africa. They are both grazers and browsers and able to eat a wide range of plants, so by choosing the transition areas between grassland and woodland, they are able to exploit both habitats very effectively. This is a great advantage, particularly during the dry season when food is short.

Dominant males attempt to hold territories of 25–100 hectares in extent. They defend these against any intruding males which attempt to usurp reproductive rights by aggressive posturing, roaring and by marking bushes on the boundaries with odoriferous secretions from glands on the head.

In the dry season, in particular, the visitor will see large herds of impala, some of which are composed of females with young, others of males only. As only the males have horns they are easily distinguished. The female herds may or may not have a mature male among them. This is because the males remain within their territories, but the females and young move from territory to territory. When the females arrive, the resident male tries to herd them and keep them within his territory, and will mate with any female in oestrus.

Within the bachelor herds there is a strict hierarchy. The younger animals are subordinate to the older, and the latter determine their position by sparring – strength and fitness being the main factors for success. When near the top of the hierarchy a male will challenge a territory-holder, and if successful, take over the harem. Defending a territory when females are within it is an exhausting business and the owner is only able to hold it for a limited period before being ousted by a fitter male. The defeated animal rejoins the bachelor herd, gradually regains his strength, and when fit enough, may challenge for a territory again.

In wetter areas, young may be born throughout the year, but in regions where seasons are more distinct there is usually a peak in October-November. Gestation is 5–6 months and the young are suckled for a similar length of time. Other species of antelope which use the harem strategy include gazelles, waterbuck and Uganda kob.

The herd e.g. buffalo

Buffalo gain much by adopting a herd strategy. There is safety in numbers, particularly as the animals are so powerful and well equipped with horns. The more vulnerable young also have a better chance of survival within the comparative safety of a herd. Although they are rather short-sighted, their senses of smell and hearing are acute, and when in a herd, the combination of all those sense organs make the group an extraordinarily alert entity. Good co-ordination of action is another advantage when danger threatens. Last, but not least, by having all ages represented, the younger animals benefit from the greater experience of their elders, both in food-finding and defence.

A buffalo herd may contain as many as 3000 animals, but in East Africa you are fortunate to see aggregations of over 1000. However, some extremely large herds occur in Kafue and South Luangwa National Parks in Zambia. Each herd is a combination of bulls, cows and calves. The bulls are usually larger, blacker and have heavier and more sweeping horns with bosses which meet at the forehead to form a bony shield. Cows are often browner and the bosses of their horns leave a gap between them.

Apart from the main herds, you come across small groups, mainly of old bulls, some looking distinctly decrepit. These are less timid than the herds with calves, and often take little notice of an approaching vehicle. With a large herd, the reaction is very different; all heads are turned towards you, bulls come to the front with muzzles raised, scenting the air, while calves become mixed up with the cows behind them. Having assessed the situation, they usually wheel round and stampede away with their attendant oxpeckers and egrets taking to the air. After a short distance, curiosity often causes them to turn again, and the older bulls may advance a few paces and reconsider the situation. If the vehicle remains still, the tension relaxes and they may continue on their way or start grazing once more.

The danger to people when on foot is not so much from the big herds, but the solitary bull lying down behind some bush or in a gully. Surprised and frightened, the animal gets to its feet and may charge instinctively. Many accidents, some fatal, have come about in this way.

There is very little aggression between members of a herd. Some bulls certainly have mating rights, status being maintained by subtle movements of the head, by odour and varying vocalisations. In this way, clashes between bulls are avoided and much energy saved.

Lion in some parks regularly kill buffalo, but these are usually ones which stray from the herd, or bulls past their prime which tend to keep on their own. In Ruwenzori National Park in Uganda, twice the number of bulls to cows are killed by lion.

In areas of greater rainfall, suitable food is more plentiful and buffaloes breed throughout the year and have smaller ranges, but where seasons are more contrasting, most calves are born during the rains and in the dry season the herds have to range more widely to find sufficient grass and water. Eland is another species which uses the herd strategy, although herd numbers are much fewer than in buffalo.

Thus in the course of several million years, a wide spectrum of herbivore species has evolved to populate the savannah with a minimum of competition between them for the abundant resources. This has been achieved by different species occupying different niches. In this way they have become adapted to a variety of habitats within the ecosystem, to different food or the means of obtaining it in each of those habitats, and to the problems of survival against extremes of climate, predation, internal parasites and disease. The herbivores have indeed been an evolutionary success story. Long may it continue.

CHAPTER 4

Giraffe

The giraffe is an improbable beast. Out of context it looks incongruous, a caricature of an animal, but in acacia savannah it fills its niche perfectly as a high-level browser. Each strange characteristic is a remarkable adaptation to this unusual lifestyle.

They are fascinating to watch at close quarters and fortunately they are usually very tolerant of vehicles. Sometimes you see a party of giraffe making their way purposefully across the plains – probably making for a new feeding area. It is rewarding to anticipate their destination and wait quietly for their arrival. In this way you can sometimes watch them feeding all around you and experience the thrill of being in close proximity to such magnificent animals.

The shape is extraordinary. The body, fore-shortened and sloping is supported on long legs, the front ones longer than the back. The incredible neck stands up like a beacon and supports a relatively small, but very heavy head, bearing short horns and a battery of highly efficient sense organs.

The neck is the key to the giraffe's success as it enables it to reach a nutritious food resource well out of reach of other herbivores, apart from those that can climb. Practically all mammals have seven neck vertebrae, whether they have short necks or long, and giraffes are no exception. During the course of evolution this great extension has been achieved by greatly elongating each neck vertebra, but the resulting increase in weight has brought many problems as head and neck together weigh about a third of a tonne in a large male.

Colossal muscles are needed to control neck movements, and these are attached to much-enlarged thoracic vertebrae which account for the strange shoulder hump which is so conspicuous.

The head is heavier than it appears from its size. The skull of a mature male may weigh as much as 15 kg, perhaps three times as much as a female's skull. This is because in the male it becomes progressively thicker with age, a characteristic correlated with the use of head and neck when fighting and determining hierarchy. Powered by the muscular neck, the head is a formidable blunt instrument for dealing sledge-hammer blows on a rival. The females do not indulge in head bashing.

The horns are unlike those of other mammals. Starting off as cartilaginous knobs at birth, they quickly become bony and fuse with the skull. In males the horns are heavier and more rounded at the tips reaching a length of about 22 cm. In both sexes the horns are covered in skin throughout life, and when young, are tipped with a tuft of black hairs. Older males soon lose these hairs, but the bone does not penetrate the skin. They usually have two horns, but in addition, older animals may acquire what appear to be a further pair behind and occasionally a medium one in front. These extra ones are outgrowths of bone from the skull.

If a giraffe is attacked by lion it will defend itself with vigorous blows of the fore legs. These are armed with formidable hooves which are up to 22 cm in diameter in a large bull. A large hoof size is a necessary adaptation for supporting the considerable weight of the animal without it sinking too far into soft ground.

The main sense organs carried some 5 m up are ideally situated for receiving long-distance messages. Eyesight is phenomenally good and giraffe are able to keep in visual contact even when more than a kilometre apart, their white ears being important visual signs. From this top-storey vantage point giraffe are also able to detect predators when still a long distance away. Hearing and smell are also acute, so the giraffe's reputation for alertness is certainly well earned.

Coat colour and pattern are very variable, and an individual retains its pattern throughout life, although its colour may darken. Typical basic patterns occur in some localities, some of which have been recognised as subspecies, but they all interbreed. The most distinctive is the reticulated giraffe, found in northern Kenya; it may be seen in parks such as Samburu, Meru and Marsabit. It has a network of narrow, white markings which separate large geometrical patches of a warm, chestnut brown colour. The most common subspecies is the Maasai giraffe which is found in southern Kenya and Tanzania. It has an irregular pattern of dark, vine-leaf or star-like patches on a lighter background. The Rothschild's or Baringo giraffe superficially resembles the reticulated, but the network pattern is buff-coloured and distinctly wider, and the legs are lighter with few spots below the knees. They occur in western Kenya and northern Uganda, although some have been translocated to Nakuru National Park. Thorneycroft's giraffe only occurs in the South Luangwa National Park in Zambia where it has been isolated for a long period and acquired a distinctive pattern.

One of the problems of having such a long neck is that it takes the head a long way from the heart. So to get blood to the brain the heart has to pump it 3 m or more against gravity. The giraffe solves this by having a massive heart weighing around 10 kg, and a left ventricle (which pumps the blood to the head and body) with a wall 8 cm thick. This generates a blood pressure 2–3 times that of ours. Moreover, the heart beat is around 150 per minute when relatively inactive. However, by the time the blood reaches the brain the pressure has dropped to a safe level due to gravity.

The biggest problem arises when the giraffe bends down to drink. Then, gravity enhances blood pressure and there is a potential danger of the brain being damaged as when somebody suffers a stroke. To prevent this happening the carotid arteries divide into a network of small arteries before reaching the brain. These have very elastic walls which can expand under pressure to the limits imposed by the bony walls surrounding the spaces in which they lie; the increase in volume reduces the pressure temporarily. However, the blood has to return to the heart in the jugular veins against gravity, so these have a series of valves which close when the neck is lowered, preventing blood from flowing back to the head. It is only when the neck is straightened again that the blood flows back once more into the heart. This explains why giraffe are reluctant to lower their necks too far, but when they have to, splay out their fore legs or bend their knees to lessen the neck angle. At the end of a drinking bout a giraffe will sway its head, pendulum-like and use the impetus generated to help lift the front of its body, enabling it to bring the front legs together and so regain an upright posture.

The neck creates a similar problem for breathing, as the lungs are such a long way from the source of air that when a breath is taken in, not all the air reaches the lungs. The lungs have to be large for such a big animal and oxygen exchange needs to be very efficient, so the red corpuscles are smaller than ours and more numerous, thus increasing the surface area for absorption.

Food and feeding behaviour

One usually associates giraffe with acacias of various kinds, and when given the choice, their nutritious leaves are a favourite food, but they also take foliage from many other trees and bushes and they occasionally eat herbaceous plants. In Zambia, in places where sausage trees are plentiful, they like to eat their pendulous flowers; they will also eat fruits of various kinds.

When feeding on acacias, the tufts of leaves they seek lodge between vicious thorns, so the tips of the thorns are eaten along with the leaves which are plucked off the stem with the lower incisors. The tongue can be extended to 45 cm and is coated with thick, viscous saliva, so the leaves can be safely withdrawn into the mouth. The last thing a giraffe wants to do is to pick up dropped leaves from the ground. The upper lip is prehensile, and when giraffe are feeding on trees with no spines, it helps to grasp bunches of leaves which are then raked off by curiously-lobed canines when the shoot is passed through the mouth.

When you see a giraffe browsing some way off you will notice that some stretch their necks as high as possible to reach the leaves, while others bend their necks and feed from above. On closer inspection you will discover that the former are males and the latter, females. This sounds like a tall story, but as a generalisation it is a true one. In fact, this difference in behaviour between the sexes is useful as it reduces the competition for food. In some parks such as Nairobi where both whistling thorn and taller acacias occur, you will find more females on the open plains where the whistling thorn is common and more males among the tall trees. Where giraffe are numerous, the browsing effect on the trees is very evident, with whistling thorn limited to 2–3 m and larger trees shaped according to the browse line at about 5 m. The giraffe's habit of not stopping at any one tree too long, prevents excessive damage and acts like a gardener with secateurs who wants to bring about more bushy growth. So more leaves become available in due course.

Giraffe feed mainly in the morning and late afternoon, but they also feed after dark. In the middle of the day and at night they have long sessions of chewing the cud (p. 31–32). They can eat as much as 50 kg of food a day, and by choosing the vegetation around water courses and where the water table is high during the dry season, are able to find fresh leaves throughout the year as trees in these habitats keep their leaves.

Rest and movement

You seldom see a giraffe sitting as this happens mainly at night. When they do sit, they tuck their legs beneath them but keep their necks upright. This is a difficult position from which to stand up and it takes time, so they are then more vulnerable to predators. Occasionally you come across a group of them sitting in a rough circle. When they do this, they choose an open situation where there is little cover, and by pointing their heads in various directions they cover the full spectrum – an excellent anti-predator device. They sleep when sitting, with head resting on flank, but only for bouts of a few minutes and then only at night.

Giraffe like to be leisurely in their movements, but they can attain a surprising 25 km per hour if necessary. When walking, both fore and hind limbs of one side are off the ground at the same time, as in camels, but when galloping, fore and hind work as pairs, the hind passing beyond and outside the fore legs and the neck swaying rhythmically backwards and forwards to preserve a perfect balance.

Social life

When somebody spots a giraffe, somebody else almost immediately sees another, and so on until seven or eight are located. This is a usual group number, but occasionally, many more may be seen together. On one memorable occasion, in a secluded part of the Serengeti, I counted 140 in quite a small area. Some were sufficiently close together to get 40 in one photograph. But these large gatherings are not cohesive groups, but aggregations of individuals brought together for some reason such as the availability of an abundance of suitable food. Surprisingly, the composition of all groups, large and small, often changes from day to day. These flexible groupings serve mainly for protection, as being spread out and having acute senses, they can readily spot predators and communicate alarm. However, groups are not quite haphazard and a number of females may share a home range of up to 120 km^2, although they mainly keep to a much smaller and favoured region within this, known as a core area. Males have smaller ranges, the size being governed by mating opportunities. Mating rights are largely restricted to dominant males which spend much time patrolling the core area used by the females, looking for any cow coming into oestrus.

Hierarchy amongst the males is usually determined at adolescence when they are 3–4 years old. This is a time when young males disperse from their parental areas and band together. Status is determined by 'necking'. This is a fascinating piece of behaviour to watch. It serves as a trial of strength – a ritualistic fight with well-respected ground rules. Two males will stand side by side facing the same or opposite directions, with legs slightly splayed for stability. They may then intertwine their necks in a most complex manner, often following this up with a series of blows of head and neck on the flanks of the other. It is all very leisurely and they take it in turns to deliver the blows. This can go on for quite a long time without much harm to either. It is likely that the contestants remember the identity of their opponents so a repeat performance becomes unnecessary.

Serious fights can take place between a dominant bull and a stranger which enters his range. Sledgehammer blows may be delivered so fiercely on flanks and belly that the sounds of impact may be heard from afar. Instances have been reported of an animal being knocked out by such punishment. The remarkable thickness of a bull's skull is clearly a necessary adaptation in this context.

Reproduction

A dominant bull discovers when a cow is coming into oestrus by testing her urine for its hormone content. He will go up to a cow, nudge her in the tail region and cause her to urinate. He then collects some urine in his mouth, raises his head and curls back his lips in a manner characteristic of many ungulates, known as flehmen. If she is in condition he will start a lengthy courtship, following her wherever she goes. Only when ready to mate will she stop and let him mount. The mating act only lasts a few seconds, but it is usually repeated several times at short intervals.

Females first conceive when around five years old, and the gestation is 15 months. They may live 25 years, so in the course of a life time may have up to 12 calves. Males become mature earlier, but they have little chance of mating until eight or nine years old as relatively few bulls reach dominant status.

Most ranges have their traditional calving areas. A cow, when birth is imminent, will move away from other females and make for such a place, and if she has had a calf before, she will probably return to the same area. Birth occurs when standing up, so the calf makes a somewhat precipitous entry into the world, breaking the umbilical cord as it falls. At birth the calf is already nearly 2 m tall and may weigh up to 60 kg, and after 15–20 minutes it is capable of getting to its feet, none the worse for its unceremonious head-first drop.

For the first few days after birth the mother keeps near her calf and suckles frequently. This is a crucial time when the mother/calf bond is forged through sight and scent, and mutual recognition is established. During this period the mother will keep other females away from her calf, but when this brief interlude is over, mother and calf will join up with others in the calving area and the calves have the chance to get to know each other. Strong bonds are forged between these youngsters by a curious 'nosing' ritual. This happens when two calves come together, nose to nose, scenting and licking each other; they then lower their heads and suddenly jump apart in a most amusing manner. Through such interactions all the young calves become bound together as a cohesive group.

It is not long before this group, first described as a 'kindergarten', is left on its own all day while the mothers move off to browse. The usual routine is for the mothers to return in the evening to suckle, stay with the calves all night and suckle again in the morning before moving off to feed once more. Being left on their own for so long obviously has its dangers, although even when the adults are widely dispersed, their eyesight is so good that they can often detect a predator in good time. This is particularly true when the kindergarten area is on a hill, as it often is. This strategy, in spite of many losses, is probably better than the random dispersal of calves – a device used by many antelope – as young giraffe are so large and difficult to hide. The calves also have the advantage when living in a kindergarten of an early-warning system provided by the combined sensory perception of the group. When the calves are about 4 months old they start to make sorties with their mothers, and soon after, will follow them all day.

As in so many species of herbivore, losses during the first year are often high; they are mainly due to predation by lion, leopard and hyaena. In the Serengeti it was calculated that 22% died during the first month, 50% in the first 6 months and 58% during the full year. Figures for some other areas are even higher. But once they are over this vulnerable period casualties become remarkably low. The growth rate of calves is phenomenal; it can be nearly a metre a year. However, they do not reach full height until 5–7 years old. Weaning takes place at 15–18 months, male calves usually before the females.

The giraffe is a successful species. Their unusual structural evolution has brought its problems, but these have been adequately solved by remarkable adaptations. At the present time it is heartening to see that they are on the increase in many of the national parks.

CHAPTER 5

Elephant

The elephant occupies a unique niche in the savannah ecosystem. Its immense size when adult, has largely freed it from predations, so although a herbivore, it stands at the top of its food chain with no enemies apart from man.

Large size brings its problems as well as advantages. A large weight has to be supported, great quantities of food are needed and temperature control becomes more difficult. But the elephant has surmounted these problems efficiently during its long period of evolution and by the time modern man had come on the scene, it had populated most of the African continent.

To support its great bulk, an elephant has huge pillar-like limbs with immensely strong leg bones, and to spread the load efficiently, it has flattened, rounded feet of large diameter – so large, that the circumference of the fore foot is approximately equal to half the shoulder height from the ground. The sole of the foot is ridged to help grip, and the bones of the foot are embedded in a large cushion of fibrous tissue which acts as a shock-absorber and enables it to move remarkably silently through the bush. An elephant usually walks very slowly, but when moving purposefully, it can increase its stride and attain a speed of 10–12 km per hour. In spite of its great weight, when it charges, it can move faster than a human can sprint.

The skull is a massive structure which has evolved to support the trunk, the heavy crushing teeth and the tusks. To lighten its weight, and so relieve some of the strain on the neck muscles, there is a network of air cavities within the skull, and the neck itself is kept short. However, its great height (up to 3·5 m), so advantageous when competing with other herbivores for food resources, has made necessary other anatomical adaptations. Of these, the trunk is the most remarkable.

The trunk is formed from the nose and upper lip and has paired nostrils throughout its length. Being composed largely of muscular tissue, it is very flexible and serves as a fifth limb which can be used for a variety of activities. It is not only an organ of great power, but can also be used for carrying out delicate operations with great precision with the help of two prehensile extensions at the tip which bear sensory hairs. Thus small fruits can be selected and plucked off spiney bushes, and seeds from acacia pods picked off the ground.

The trunk is an essential tool when feeding as it allows an elephant to reach vegetation from ground level to more than 5 m up, and to stretch over bushes to obtain material well out of reach of other browsers. It can also curl its trunk round a bough and break it off to bring leaves within its reach.

When an elephant drinks, the trunk is used like a straw for sucking up the water before squirting it down its throat; it can suck up four litres at a time. It also breathes through its trunk, and when in water, may use it as a snorkel. By this means, an elephant can cross extensive stretches of water, if not too deep. This ability accounts for their occasional presence on islands as much as a kilometre from a lake shore. Presumably they are attracted by the smell of unexploited vegetation.

After drinking, an elephant may use its trunk to squirt mud over itself and then complete its toiletry with a thorough dusting of dry soil. This causes the animal to take on the colour of the region – very obvious with the 'red' elephants of Tsavo. This muddying and dusting helps to rid the sensitive skin of parasites, as they become embedded in the dried mud along with abrasive sand particles and are crushed when the elephant rubs itself against a tree trunk or termite mound.

An elephant smells through its trunk, and when alarmed, raises it like the spout of a Victorian coffee pot to test the air. It can twist the end in any direction and so determine the direction of the threat.

The trunk may also be used for various social interactions. When adults meet after a period of separation, they will intertwine their trunks in greeting, or place the tip of the trunk into the other's mouth. A young calf also finds out much about food selection before it is weaned by putting its trunk into its mother's mouth to sample the contents. The trunk is also used to guide, support and encourage a young calf, just as a human mother would use her arm with a child.

In contrast, the trunk may be used as a weapon. In Ruwenzori National Park there was an elephant which regularly used to go the rounds of the dustbins near the research station. One particularly dark night, a Congolese, who helped us in the house, walked out of the lighted bungalow into the darkness and went straight into this elephant. It smote him across the face with its trunk, knocking him down and loosening his front teeth. Fortunately, he was more frightened than badly hurt, but it could have been serious. Elephants which become used to people are always potentially dangerous and should be treated with great caution.

Temperature control

One of the consequences of being large, is the danger of overheating. A small animal loses heat rapidly as its surface to volume ratio is large, but a big one is slow to cool down after exertion especially under hot conditions. The problem is compounded when the body is dark in colour, as more of the sun's heat is absorbed, and having no sweat glands, an elephant cannot lose heat that way. So it solves the problem by having huge ears which act as radiators and by behavioural adaptations.

The skin on the underside of the ears is thin, and below it there is a network of blood vessels through which warm blood passes. When it flaps its ears, two things happen. The surface area of its body is increased by a third when the backs of the ears and the area they cover are exposed, and cooler air is brought close to the blood vessels. This device is so effective that the temperature of the blood leaving the ear may be up to 19°C cooler than when it entered. Elephants will also stand down wind to allow the breeze to reach the backs of their ears, but on a cold morning, will keep the ears tightly against the body. As the day heats up, ear flapping becomes more persistent. They will also squirt mud or water behind their ears, where evaporation will cause cooling.

Elephants habitually use shade during the middle of the day, moving as little as possible to minimise the heat generated. In regions where they have destroyed many shade trees, the calves, in particular, may suffer considerable stress. When conditions become very hot, elephants like to move to marshy areas or bathe in lakes or rivers, squirting water over themselves and lying on their sides to allow a larger surface area of skin to be cooled.

Water appears to be thoroughly enjoyed by elephants. One November in Samburu, we were caught in torrential rain while on a game run. The hard ground was quickly flooded, so that bushes stood out like islands in a lake, and the surface of the ground became very muddy. Proceeding cautiously, as the track was very slippery, we came on a herd of about 50 elephants just having fun. Some were lying down in the mud and rolling over with legs in the air to get every part covered; others were squirting trunkfulls of mud over themselves and each other. One matriarch was vigorously rubbing her immense bottom against a small tree after muddying herself, and a youngster joined her and tried to do the same from the other side. Their backsides kept hitting each other, and the tree swayed drunkenly from side to side. The whole episode was a wonderful exhibition of uninhibited behaviour in the rain.

Dentition

The tusks are modified upper incisors which grow throughout life. They are used when fighting, for manipulating boughs, prising off bark and digging. They are usually asymmetrical, differing both in shape and alignment – a useful guide to the identity of individuals in the field. Just as we are right- or left-handed, so elephants have their favourite tusk, and you can often tell which it is by the extra wear. Elephants which only have one tusk have usually broken the other one, but some are tuskless from birth. This is a genetic condition which is common in areas, such as the South Luangwa National Park in Zambia.

Few large tuskers occur today due to relentless poaching for ivory, but in the past a tusk has been known to reach 3.5 m in length and a pair weigh 200 kg. Tusks of females are much smaller and lighter, seldom exceeding 9 kg.

The crushing teeth are massive structures measuring as much as 30 x 7 cm; they have diamond-shaped ridges on their grinding surfaces. During the course of its life, an elephant may use up to 24 of these great teeth, six on each half of both jaws, but not more than two teeth in each half jaw are in use at a time. Every tooth erupts at the back of the jaw and gradually moves forwards as the one in front wears down. It eventually drops out when it reaches the front. The first batch of four is shed when the calf is two years old, and the last drops out around the end of its life, when 65–70.

Food and feeding behaviour

We have already seen that an elephant's great height, combined with its versatile trunk, enables it to reach vegetation from ground level up to more than 5 metres. But an elephant also has the advantage over rival herbivores of being able to feed on poor quality, coarse material which is available all year round. Although digestion is inefficient, it can take in vast quantities of food by way of compensation, feeding 16 hours out of the 24 in order to do so. An adult is capable of putting away 270 kg of vegetation a day, although 150 kg is more usual. For those who are astonished how much food a human family can eat each week, it might be of interest that during a life-time a single elephant may consume as much as 4,000 tonnes! So the depredations of a large herd can hardly be imagined.

Elephants do not chew the cud, and most of the digestion takes place in the caecum, a large, blind sac which extends from the junction of the small and large intestines. Here, symbiotic bacteria break down the cellulose and lignin.

An elephant's diet includes the leaves of many herbaceous and woody species. During the rains they feed mainly on grasses, but when these have dried out, they browse more on coarser leaves, twigs, boughs and bark. They are also fond of succulent fruits and the pods of acacias when these become ripe.

It is fascinating to watch elephants feeding: to see one wrap its trunk around a tuft of grass, loosen it with a nudge from a foot, pull it up by the roots, then pause to shake off the loose soil before stuffing it into its mouth; or to watch one standing, almost on tiptoe, to reach up with its trunk to grasp a bunch of leaves far above its head.

Elephants can go as long as four days without water, but usually drink every day if it is easily available. Water quality is of little consequence; those that drink at Kilaguni appear to enjoy the effluent from the Lodge's laundry. They need on average 70–90 litres each day, and when food becomes scarce near a water supply and they are forced to go far to find it, they may walk as much as 40 km in a day in order to drink.

When rivers run dry, elephants use their tusks and trunks to dig small wells. Although desperate for water, they do not hurry to take a first trunkfull, but wait until the sand particles have settled before sucking it up. If the water is far down, calves cannot reach it, so the mother will fill her trunk and squirt it down the youngster's throat. When the river dried up at Samburu on one occasion, elephants dug numerous wells in its sandy bed and many antelopes, particularly waterbuck and impala, made use of them after the elephants had slaked their thirst.

Social life

Elephants have a complex social system. The basic unit is the cow and her calves, but this becomes extended when her calves also have young. She then becomes the matriarch of the group. The matriarch may be recognised as the largest (and oldest) female in the group. Sometimes, larger groups may occur in which there is no obvious matriarch but there are several females of about the same size along with their calves. This can happen if matriarchs die and nearly related families join up.

A herd will roam over a home range of up to 1500 km^2 in arid districts, but where food is plentiful, they move far less. It is the matriarch's experience of this large area, built up over many decades, that is so valuable to the group. She knows the best feeding areas, where fruit is seasonally abundant, the location of water, where to go in times of drought, and places of danger to be avoided. Tragically, where poaching is rife, it is the adults that are killed for their ivory, so in addition to breaking up the units with devastating effects on family life, the young are robbed of the experience so essential for survival.

Closely related family groups sometimes join up temporarily to form large aggregations called kinship groups, and when under stress or making seasonal movements, even larger herds may be formed. At Amboseli, one January, we were fortunate to see a herd of 2–300 moving into the area. It was extremely impressive to see these great animals moving on a broad front in distinct waves, each probably a kinship group. Males were mixed in with the others, including some in the vanguard of the advancing army. Slowly, but steadily they plodded on towards a large area where coarse grasses were abundant and water available. It is sad that scenes such as this are seldom, if ever, seen today, numbers having been so ruthlessly decimated by poachers.

The family unit is well co-ordinated. The matriarch decides the daily routine, such as where to go, when to move towards water, when to find shade and when to sleep. Once a route has been determined, it takes a lot to make her change her mind. This behavioural characteristic can be put to advantage when watching elephants. At Samburu we encountered a herd of 16, including calves just over a year old. Getting in front of their casual progress, and turning off the engine, we just waited in silence. Treating us as part of the landscape, they slowly approached, browsing as they came. They passed within a few metres of the vehicle on either side of us making us feel almost part of the herd. It was a moving experience to have these great animals so close, with tiny calves raising their small trunks inquiringly as they passed.

On another occasion we saw elephants bunching on the river bank. They were not drinking, so we thought they might be about to cross. Gradually numbers built up until over 30 had gathered. By parking as near as possible, but to one side, we were able to witness the crossing from close quarters. A matriarch stepped in first and tentatively tested the depth of the water and the firmness of the bottom with a front foot. Finding the going satisfactory, she slowly waded out into the river, followed by an older calf. One by one the others followed, head to tail, in a long line. The youngest, about 2 years old, found the going hard, as the water reached up to its ears, but one adult went alongside and another guided it from behind with her trunk, and it safely reached the far bank

Getting close to elephants, in places where they are used to vehicles, is usually quite safe, but it should only be attempted by experienced rangers who know the animals. This was brought home to me in Ruwenzori National Park when we came across an elephant which saw us from quite a distance and immediately charged. It was not difficult to take avoiding action, so we watched it from a long way away, intrigued by its unusual behaviour. Soon another car came along the track and was immediately given the same treatment. Clearly the animal was a source of potential danger, so it was put under surveillance by a ranger. It made further charges, and eventually had to be shot. It was found that its hide was peppered with shot-gun wounds, so presumably it had previously been attacked from a vehicle, and had associated that traumatic experience with cars and was out for revenge.

A family group shows much co-operative behaviour. If danger is detected, they all bunch together with the adults facing the threat and the calves in the centre. Small calves always get much care and attention from mothers and elder sisters, and when on the move in difficult terrain, they will give assurance to a calf by caressing or guiding it with a trunk, and if it falls, will get it to its feet again by using trunk or foot. The strength of family bonds is also demonstrated when an adult is dying; all gather round, and every effort is made to raise it to its feet. It has even been known for another to force food into the dying one's mouth in an attempt to revive it. The same sort of thing happens if an adult is shot; others will immediately surround it, regardless of danger to themselves, but unfortunately this behaviour plays into the hands of poachers, who are thus provided with further targets.

Sleeping is another activity which is synchronised. Sound sleep lasts for 1–4 hours and takes place in the early hours. Very large animals usually remain standing, others lie on their sides; they often snore loudly. Occasionally they will sleep during the day, but only for short cat naps; you see an eye close, then the trunk hangs loose and the animal remains motionless for a few minutes.

In contrast to the tight, cohesive female groups, males form much looser aggregations the composition of which is frequently changing. Young males leave the family units at puberty and join up temporarily with other males of varying ages, but some large males are solitary for much of the time except when they visit female groups for mating.

Young males quickly establish hierarchy by sparring. These push-and-shove bouts, with tusks interlocked, are trials of strength and seldom lead to injury, but older bulls may fight with great ferocity over a female in oestrus. If they are evenly matched, the combat can go on for several hours and involve charges, head to head shoving, and wrestling with trunks and tusks. Fatalities occasionally occur, but usually the one which tires first, breaks away and leaves the victor to mate undisturbed.

Communication

This is an important aspect of social behaviour. When elephants are near together, changes in the position of the head, ears, trunk and tail convey mood and intentions, but scent also plays an important part in recognising individuals and assessing their sexual status. This was vividly illustrated when we came across a female in Ruwenzori National Park which had given birth a few hours previously. She stood with her tiny calf in the centre of a large clearing with other members of her group browsing on surrounding bushes. Then a very large bull appeared in the distance and made his way purposefully towards the cow and calf. Raising his trunk, he smelt the cow's hindquarters and then scented the baby all over most carefully. It appeared to us to be a ritual recognition ceremony.

Vocal signals play a major part in communication. When foraging in bushy savannah or at night, elephants keep in touch with low growls. These are not tummy rumbles as was first thought, but originate in the larynx and are produced consciously as a means of communication. Family groups keep up long-running conversations in this manner, which appear to be much more than contact calls. But the great mystery has been how elephants can co-ordinate their activities from a distance. A group may browse contentedly for hours on end, and suddenly, without a sound, move purposefully in a particular direction. You follow, and find that they meet up with another group, perhaps a few kilometres away and down wind. How did they know the other group was there? Watch a herd approaching a water hole; they all stop as if a command has been given, ears are raised slightly and they appear to be listening – perhaps for a minute or more. You hear no sound, see no cause for the stoppage, but some message appears to have been received.

It is now known that in addition to the low sounds we can hear, elephants can produce and hear infra-sound more than an octave below these sounds. These lower sounds, because of their low frequency, are not easily absorbed by thick vegetation, and may be heard by other elephants up to 4 km away. So, family groups well out of sight and smell distance can co-ordinate their activities, and others can respond to distress calls from far away or to the calls of females in oestrus.

Experiments have been done to prove how effective infra-sound communication can be. Recordings of these sounds made by a female in oestrus were played back to two bulls from a vehicle, parked well out of sight and up wind. On hearing the recordings, the bulls immediately headed in the direction of the sound. They arrived at the vehicle ten minutes later, no doubt disappointed that instead of an oestrus female there was merely a truck.

Infra sound is of the greatest importance in areas where elephant populations are low, and in forests where sight and sound are less effective. It also enables a male to save much energy when searching for females in oestrus; instead of visiting a number of widely scattered family groups, he can simply be on the alert for any calls females in oestrus may make. This is valuable, as a cow may only come into oestrus for a few days every four years.

Reproduction

Although males can become mature at 12, it is unlikely that they will become sufficiently dominant to mate before their mid-twenties. A female may become receptive when as young as nine and have a calf by the time she is 11 (gestation is 22 months). Thereafter, if conditions are good, she may have a calf every four years. If overcrowding occurs, or conditions are stressful for other reasons, the intervals between calves is extended and the young become mature later.

Climatic conditions may influence the onset of oestrus. During a long dry season, stress may prevent ovulation, and it may take a month or so of good feeding during the rains before oestrus occurs. So under these circumstances, conception takes place in the second half of the wet season and the calf will be born towards the beginning of the rains, nearly two years later. This is the best season for having a baby.

Males go through a period of musth during which they are in a highly sexual state. At this time, secretion from the temporal gland behind the eye flows conspicuously down the side of the face. This is caused by a rise in the level of testosterone (male hormone) in the blood. This makes them excited and aggressive, and anxious to find females in oestrus. As mentioned earlier, infra sound signals from receptive females bring these males to the family groups where mating takes place.

When we were watching elephants at Mountain Lodge, two family groups came out of the forest to drink. We assumed there was a female in oestrus among them, as two large males, both in musth, arrived at the scene from different directions. This caused chaos among the groups which split ranks when one bull tried to chase off the other with screams and flapping ears. Eventually the smaller bull fled back into the forest, leaving the other one in charge, but in a very bad temper.

A calf at birth weighs about 120 kg, and as it is born when the mother is standing, its entry into the world is dramatic to say the least. Others in the family group show great interest in the new arrival, scenting and touching it with their trunks and helping it to its feet. At first the baby stands stock still, legs apart, looking like a toy that has just been carefully placed there beside its huge mother.

The mother's breasts are between her forelegs, and a baby, well short of a metre tall, has difficulty in reaching them at first. It sucks with its mouth, the trunk being thrown over its back to get it out of the way. A calf may be suckled for years, even after the mother has had her next calf, but with older calves, sucking is opportunistic and not essential, as by the time they are two years old they can feed wholly on solids if necessary.

It takes time for a tiny calf to learn what to do with its trunk. When it runs, the trunk wobbles about as if out of control, and when the group go to drink, it cannot use it like an adult, but has to lie down in the water and drink directly through its mouth.

An elephant has the longest childhood of any animal apart from humans. This enables it to build up essential experience, and accounts for its undoubted intelligence. During this long period, it reaps the benefits of the mother's help and protection, and the attentions of aunts and older sisters who also do their share of nannying. So it grows up in a family atmosphere and quickly learns its place in the social system.

When watching family groups, there are some useful indicators for assessing age. If a calf can pass under its mother's body it is less than a year; when you see the first signs of a tusk externally, it is two; and when the tusks are judged to be 15 cm long, the youngster is 4–5 years old. Growth continues throughout life, so the largest animals are usually the oldest.

Effects of elephants on the ecosystem

When elephants are in correct balance with their environment, they contribute to the common good. Their droppings not only fertilise the soil, but also provide food for dung feeders and those dependent on them. As a single elephant can produce 40 tons of droppings per year, the effect of a group is considerable. The dung also contains the undigested seeds of many plants which become dispersed in this way. This is very obvious at Samburu where elephants are fond of the fruits of doum palms and the young plants may be seen in great numbers in places where elephants frequently foregather.

Elephants trample coarse vegetation into the ground and so enrich the soil and reduce the evaporation of moisture from it. This action also causes some grasses to sprout tender shoots to the benefit of other herbivores. When elephants knock down trees, they favour the growth of grasses, which again benefits the grazers, and by making tracks through otherwise impenetrable scrub, they allow the entry of other species to new food resources. Being careless feeders, they also provide left-overs for duikers and dik-diks, and in droughts they save the lives of others by digging wells in river beds.

Now that elephants are largely confined to the parks, they can no longer easily make seasonal movements for alternative food supplies, so they stay in a smaller area in relative safety and their numbers build up to beyond the carrying capacity of the land; this may cause great habitat destruction. With lack of food and water, they break down more trees, and by stripping bark they make those that survive more vulnerable to fire. So elephants and fire together are a deadly combination, as good cover for other animals is eliminated, erosion takes place when the rains come, and desertification may follow. In South Luangwa National Park you can see miles of mopane forest reduced to dead and dying trees due to elephant activity, and in Tsavo, few large trees remain unscathed. It is ironical that habitat destruction today in some parks is less than previously because of the wholesale slaughter of elephants by poachers.

Poaching is a matter of gravest concern. It is estimated that 80% of ivory from Africa has been obtained illegally, and the seriousness of the problem can be judged by the stark figures. In 1973, in Kenya alone, there were 167,000 elephants, by 1980 the population had been reduced to 60,000, and by 1989 to 17,000. In East Africa generally, the population is now less than half it was just 10 years ago. Over Africa as a whole, even with stocks already so depleted, it is estimated that between 50,000 and 150,000 elephants are killed each year. A measure of the decline in numbers of mature animals is demonstrated by reduction in tusk size. In 1979 a tonne of exported ivory represented 54 dead elephants, mainly males; by 1987 the corresponding number was 113, many of which were females. One also has to remember that when females are killed their calves are often left to die.

For many years anti-poaching measures have been taken and commendable success achieved by small groups of dedicated people, but such work is dangerous and extremely difficult as areas are often vast, terrain difficult and resources pitifully inadequate. More recently, with considerable support from conservation bodies and more vigorous governmental backing, these measures have been stepped up and much greater success achieved; but poaching will only be beaten when ivory is no longer a profitable business investment, demand for the product is drastically reduced, prices fall and the rewards become insignificant in proportion to the risks.

Bans on the ivory trade and other legislation will help the situation considerably, but it is the enforcement that is crucial. Success will depend upon the determination of all countries concerned to deal with corruption wherever it may be without fear or favour. Some countries have already demonstrated their determination to do this, but they need the world-wide support of all who care for this magnificent animal. It is unthinkable that the greed and irresponsibility of the few should lead to the extinction of the elephant in Africa.

CHAPTER 6

Pigs and Primates

Perhaps it sounds rather odd to put pigs and primates together in this chapter, but they do have one important characteristic in common, a diet which is basically vegetarian but supplemented with animal material – the proportion varying according to species and opportunity. This is a good formula for success allowing them to fill further niches in the savannah ecosystem.

Pigs

There are several species of pig in East Africa, but only one, the warthog, is a true savannah species; the others are forest forms and will be discussed in the appropriate chapter.

Warthog

The warthog is one of the quainter characters one meets on the savannah. It is a delightful sight to see a sow with her family of piglets in line astern with the boar protecting the rear, all running at speed with tails held vertically, their tufted tips looking like pennants in the breeze. Such a sight always conjures up a smile, but to the warthogs it may have more serious overtones as they may be fleeing from danger. The name is appropriate as they have tough wart-like outgrowths on their faces which are more prominent in adult males.

When rival males fight they may come into headlong collision and the warts may give protection against the other's tusks.

Although vulnerable to predation – lion and leopard love them – they are strong stocky animals capable of a good speed when running for home, and the formidable tusks can do a lot of damage to a predator. The upper tusks in the boar may be as long as 60 cm, but the lower, shorter ones are sharper and may do even greater injury. Warthogs largely depend on their senses of smell and hearing for detecting danger as their eyesight is rather poor.

Warthogs are not ruminants and have a simple stomach. They are less omnivorous than most pigs, but will take some animal matter occasionally including carrion, but primarily they are grazers. They use their sharp incisors to bite off the shorter grasses, will eat their seeds and dig up their rhizomes using the tough upper edge of their snout to lever them up. They do not use their tusks for this purpose. The muscles of the neck need to be particularly strong when rooting with their snouts, so the neck is thick and short, but this can sometimes be a disadvantage when feeding and the warthog compensates by kneeling. To save getting up repeatedly it may shuffle along in the kneeling position.

You sometimes find warthogs in remarkably dry savannah, but they prefer habitats with a good water supply. After rain they like nothing better than to roll in a mud wallow and smother their bodies in a shiny glutinous covering – undoubtedly a warthog's idea of bliss.

Warthogs are gregarious, the basic unit being the family party, known as a sounder, but this can be enlarged to include more than one adult female and young of various ages. Sounders can come together to form even larger aggregates, but these are transient. In addition, some older boars are solitary and you occasionally see small bachelor groups. A sounder may have a home range of up to 4 km^2 which is marked with secretions from glands near the eyes.

They are sexually mature late in their second year, but males have little opportunity of mating until about four years old. In courtship a male produces sexually attractive scents from glands on the lip. He prods the sow's flanks with his snout, sniffs her genital region and repeatedly rests his chin on her rump, all the time making regular grunting noises. Mating can last as long as ten minutes.

Up to four piglets are born in an underground burrow, often an old aardvark hole enlarged for the purpose. A sow has only two pairs of teats and when suckling, each piglet has its own teat. Piglets follow their mother when she goes foraging when about seven weeks old and they are weaned at about three months. They are driven off by the sow when she has her next litter, but often rejoin her when the new piglets are older.

Savannah primates

Two kinds of monkey are commonly seen in savannah, baboons and vervet monkeys. They have the great advantage of being as much at home in trees as on the ground and so can exploit a more varied food supply and use trees as a refuge from terrestrial predators. A third species, the patas monkey, is more local and uncommon. These species are highly intelligent, learn quickly and live in complex societies.

Baboons

The two species commonly seen in East Africa are both very powerful animals. The olive baboon is the heavier and has a greyish-olive coat; it is the commoner species in Kenya. The yellow baboon has rather longer legs and a slimmer body, and the fur is yellower and paler on the belly; they are commoner in east Kenya and much of Tanzania. Both species have dog-like faces, and when they yawn, which they frequently do, you see their large canines and a formidable battery of grinding teeth behind. Their eyes are set close together and protected by prominent brow ridges. Males are much larger than females and when mature have a thick mantle of hair over head, shoulders and upper back – particularly obvious in olive baboons.

Baboons often associate with lodges and get so tame that visitors are well advised to take precautions. They should never be fed, and when a bedroom is vacated it is wise to shut the windows. I was reminded of this at Seronera when my wife and I retired to our second-floor bedroom for a siesta. It was very hot and I opened the sliding windows. Flat on my back and half asleep, I heard a noise in the bathroom. I sat up to find a large male baboon standing near the bottom of the bed examining some equipment. We shouted at it and waved our arms, but instead of rushing to escape, it was very aggressive, baring its teeth and making angry grunts. We did get it out, but having shut the window it continued to grimace and pound the glass with its fists. It was then that I remembered the noise from the bathroom and went to investigate. To my dismay, there was another baboon, which leapt on to a high shelf, knocking things over and making a mess everywhere. I shut it in, opened the outer door to the corridor and carefully opened the bathroom door slightly. Fortunately, the baboon made a dash for the open door and was away. The male's reluctance to leave was now clear, the one in the bathroom was a female and we had prevented him from going to her aid. That same afternoon a baboon visited another bedroom and when discovered, had unzipped the pocket of a flight bag, extracted a watch and was about to make off with a passport. Their curiosity and intelligence should not be under-estimated.

The basic diet of baboons is vegetarian, and includes a lot of grass taken at different stages of growth. They eat it when the leaves are green and nutritious and later take the flower heads and ripe seeds, and when it is straw-like and inedible, they will use their strong hands to dig for the succulent rhizomes below the surface. They are very fond of fruit, particularly figs. When these are ripe a tree may attract 30 or more baboons at a time – all busily eating and temporarily storing the excess in their cheek pouches. These pouches, which have a capacity equal to that of the stomach, pass from the cheeks down the neck. They are particularly useful when eating has to be done in a hurry.

The amount of animal food baboons take varies greatly according to opportunity and the traditions of a particular troop. Some troops are largely vegetarian, others actively hunt for prey; more often they take animals if they happen to come across them when foraging. Rodents, other small mammals, hares and the young of small antelopes may be killed for food. When baboons hunt deliberately, a number of males may spread out and even encircle small prey to facilitate capture. Adult males will also rob leopards and cheetahs of their kills, these cats rarely standing their ground in the face of combined aggression.

Being social animals, they have many methods of communication. Vocalisations are very varied, ranging from the quiet exchanges between near neighbours to the noise they make when they quarrel or if a predator approaches their trees at night. If you are awoken by these discordant noises, your imagination runs riot until you realise the din is only made by baboons. Interactions between individuals involve much body language. They express their intentions and emotions by yawning, grinning, raising the eyebrows, smacking the lips and moving the ears.

Their social system is very complex. The troop, which is a large social group of 30–150 animals, is a highly organised society. Each member is well known to everybody else, and by doing so much in each other's company they learn skills from one another and attain a high level of co-operation.

The troop is composed of a number of units, each consisting of several females with their young, along with one or more adult males. From an early age, females which grow up in each other's company develop strong, long-lasting bonds and remain together, each with her own progeny. This provides a stable nucleus for the unit which can include representatives of up to three generations. The system is perpetuated as female progeny normally remain within their natal unit for the whole of their lives. Members of a unit tend to keep near each other within the troop and do things together; for example, they will choose the same part of a tree for sleeping and will more readily come to the aid of a member of their unit than to an outsider.

Male society is much less stable. Young males leave the troop when they become mature and some adults may switch from one troop to another. Each time a male joins a troop it has to insinuate its way by subtle manoeuvres before becoming accepted. At first he keeps to the periphery of the troop and tentatively tries to cultivate the attention of some adult female. He sits near her, follows her around and if tolerated, is allowed to groom her. This may continue for many weeks before she and the other females in the group take his presence for granted and accept him as a member of the unit. In this way special relationships develop between males and females within a unit.

Females have their first oestrus when about four years old. This is a very conspicuous condition as the skin below the tail becomes very pink and greatly swollen. When ready to mate, she will solicit a male by presenting her backside towards him and raise her tail. She will mate with a number of different males during the course of oestrus. Gestation is about six months, and the baby has black hair, a pink face and conspicuous pink ears. The sight of a new-born baby is a great attraction to others in the troop, especially the females, which gather round making low grunting noises and trying to groom the mother or touch the baby. Early on, the baby is carried under the body of the mother, clinging tightly to her fur, but by about five weeks, it is able to ride on her back like a jockey. At about this age it is active enough to start playing. Play gradually increases in vigour as it grows up.

Play is an important feature in the lives of juveniles. If you see a number playing, switch off the engine and take time to watch their antics. They soon take no notice of your presence and if you are fortunate, will give an uninhibited display of acrobatics which is hard to beat. Such play gives splendid training in muscular development and co-ordination which prepares them for more serious activities later on in life.

On one occasion we were watching a troop of baboons in Zambia as they came towards the river. During the previous wet season, the swollen river had eroded the bank leaving a vertical sandy ridge about 5 m high with a sandy beach below. The game started when a few juveniles jumped off the ridge and raced up again to have another go. Soon they were all at it, trying to push one another over the edge, leaping off the bank and turning somersaults in mid air, chasing, jumping and wrestling in the soft sand. This must have gone on non-stop for twenty minutes. Suddenly, as if a whistle had been blown, the whole troop stopped playing and hurried away, leaving the beach strangely quiet after all the hectic activity.

Troops occupy large home ranges, sometimes up to 40 km². These contain the main requisites for survival – convenient trees for sleeping in safety, good feeding areas, and a reliable source of water. Baboons need to drink frequently. The ranges are not actively defended and there is overlap between neighbouring troops, but they try to avoid each other.

By living in a troop, baboons get good protection from predators. Their combined alertness gives early warning of danger, and a bark from one, alerts the whole troop. Adult males may combine to intimidate a single predator, but with lion they will usually flee and climb the nearest convenient tree.

On one occasion at Samburu, we heard a lot of barking coming from some way off and decided to investigate. At first, we saw little except for a group of trees on the horizon which appeared to be full of vultures. However, on getting close, our vultures turned out to be 60–80 baboons, and there was a lioness on the ground below watching them. She had a bloody nose, and we assumed she had already killed and eaten one of their number. The baboons were barking excitedly and jumping from branch to branch in great agitation showing much aggression. The lioness prowled below, hoping no doubt for a false step by one of the more daring individuals leaping about just out of reach.

Vervet and Patas monkeys

These two species are closely related, but Patas monkeys are larger, have longer legs and their upper parts are distinctly reddish. They prefer living in open acacia woodland and spend more time on the ground than vervets. They can run extremely fast to escape danger and take refuge up trees.

Vervets are medium-sized monkeys, agile, alert and mischievous, with black faces, outlined in white, light greyish or olive fur except on the belly where it is white, and a long tail. They prefer more wooded areas than Patas monkeys, such as forest edges and woody savannah. They are excellent climbers, spending much of their time in trees, but groom, play and forage on the ground as well.

Both species rely considerably on plant food such as grass, flowers, leaves and fruits of many kinds, acacia pods being particularly favoured. They will supplement their diet with insects and other invertebrates, lizards and even birds' eggs. Vervets, in particular, are quick to exploit any food source and may show much cunning, coming into the dining rooms of lodges and running off with anything edible before they are chased away.

Both species are social. Vervets usually live in groups of about ten animals which may include several adult males. Patas monkeys form rather larger groups, but they contain only a single adult male. Both are diurnal and sleep in trees, but Patas monkeys have the unusual habit of each member of the group having its own tree and these may be quite some distance from each other. This is possibly an anti-predator device.

CHAPTER 7

Carnivores of the Savannah: the Large Cats

The savannah is very rich in carnivore species. With so many herbivores around of varying sizes, there is much scope for predation. The members of the order, Carnivora, which are more likely to be seen on safari in East Africa, are classified in five families:

1. The cats: lion, leopard, cheetah, caracal, serval and wild cat.
2. The dogs: hunting dogs, three species of jackal – black backed, golden and side-striped – and bat-eared foxes.
3. The hyaenas: spotted and striped hyaena and aardwolf.
4. The viverrids: genet, civet, and six species of mongoose – dwarf, banded, slender, marsh, white tailed and great grey.
5. The mustelids: ratel (honey badger) and zorilla.

Like the herbivores, these species exploit different niches, and so lessen the competition between them for the available resources. They do this by feeding on different prey, using different hunting techniques, occupying different habitats and by hunting at different times. Each species has its particular mode of life, its characteristic diet and its own specialised techniques for obtaining food; so it is not surprising that they differ in size, shape and dexterity. Those which feed on large herbivores, for example, look very different from those which are mainly insectivorous. Nevertheless, all carnivores have characteristics in common.

The characteristics of carnivores

Mammals which feed on the bodies of other animals consume a very nutritious, concentrated product which is easily digested and supplies a lot of energy. The only snag is that the prey has to be caught before it is eaten, so the structure of a carnivore has to be geared to that necessity. Thus all have specially developed structures for capturing and killing the prey, and very acute sense organs for finding them.

Moving prey is more difficult to capture than one that is still, so all carnivores tend to have their eyes facing forwards; this gives them a degree of binocular vision which helps them judge distances more accurately. In addition, some large carnivores such as lions have their eyes particularly well adapted for savannah conditions where the prey is often seen first as a long line on the horizon. In most mammals there is a circular area in the centre of the retina which gives the most detailed vision, but in the lion this takes the form of a linear strip which copes best with horizontal images.

Hearing is also extremely important in locating prey and is particularly well developed in cats such as the serval, which hunt in long grass likely to hide its prey completely. Bat-eared foxes are dependent on their marvellous hearing for detecting the movements of insects below ground.

The sense of smell is very valuable, especially to those like the genet which often hunt by following the scent trails of their prey. Scent is also used as an important means of communication between members of the same species.

The dentition of carnivores is well adapted for both killing and biting. In the cats, the canines are the main killing instruments, although in other carnivores their functions may be more general. Some species have sharp, slicing molars called carnassials, which cut the flesh into manageable portions for swallowing; they are very well developed in the larger carnivores.

Nearly all carnivores are to some extent scavengers on prey caught by others, and will also eat carrion; others will supplement their more typical diet with plant foods, especially fruits of many kinds. In this chapter, the varying life styles and adaptations of the large cats will be considered in more detail.

Cheetah

Everybody wants to see a cheetah, and no wonder, because it is the essence of feline grace – imperious, aloof and beautiful to behold. Its spotted coat differs from a leopard's by having single spots, not clusters, and the 'tear marks' on its relatively small head are diagnostic. Research scientists distinguish individuals by a combination of the spot pattern on the face, the position of scars and ear nicks, and the type of ring pattern on the tail.

If you are looking for cheetah, it is helpful to understand the timetable they often follow. Their most active time is from dawn until mid-morning when it is becoming too hot for comfort. An early morning game drive is highly recommended as it is then that you are likely to see them on the move as they search for possible prey. However, when really hungry, they will hunt at any time if the opportunity arises. In the middle of the day, they like to rest in shade, so you find them under isolated trees on the plains, or among bushes elsewhere; however, they are not easy to spot from a distance as they are often lying down. During the rains and when the grass is long, finding them is much more difficult as they can rest practically anywhere and be completely hidden. It is always worthwhile keeping an eye on any termite mounds which project above the grass as they use these as look-outs. There is also a more active period in the late afternoon, particularly if the cheetah has failed to kill during the morning.

Their favourite habitat is the open plain and their most important prey, the Thomson's gazelle, so the place to look for them is where there are good numbers of these small antelopes grazing on short sward. You can certainly find them in more scrubby areas, but only where they can rely on vision to locate their prey.

The cheetah is a true cat, although it differs from the others by having non-retractile claws. It is built for speed over short distances – a sprinter, not a long-distance runner. Its long slender legs are powered by well-developed shoulder muscles, and its deep chest houses large lungs. The small head is rounded, and the eyes point forward to give excellent binocular vision. This is a great advantage as sight is all important for a diurnal hunter. The nose is small, possibly because, if it were larger, it would limit the advantage of the binocular vision by getting in the way; the sense of smell is less acute in consequence.

Food and hunting behaviour.

Cheetahs feed on a variety of small antelopes and the young of larger ones, but Thomson's gazelles are their mainstay in most parts of their range. They also take Grant's gazelle, reedbuck and impala, but mainly the juveniles. Anything bigger than 50 kg cannot be tackled by a single animal, but by working together in twos or threes, cheetah may kill larger animals such as gnus. Hares, if disturbed in the grass, are taken quite often, and in more scrubby areas, dikdik and young gerenuk may be hunted. They also kill game birds such as francolin and spurfowl.

When a cheetah is searching for prey, it may travel 3–10 km in a day. On coming to an area where 'Tommies' are grazing, it may either settle and wait for them to graze nearer, or it will stalk them. A hunt is only successful if it can overtake its prey before it gets out of breath – a 500-metre sprint is about its limit.

Having stalked as near as possible without being detected, eyes fixed on the selected animal and head and body low to the ground, it suddenly springs forward, reaching perhaps 80 k.p.h. in a few strides. The back is wonderfully supple, and the body appears to extend and recoil in rhythmic sequence as it bears down on the prey. The Tommie tries to zigzag, and when nearly caught, a sudden turn can gain it a few metres because the cheetah cannot alter course so easily, but the gap closes again, the Tommie's flank is struck by a fore paw and it crashes to the ground. Immediately, the cheetah goes for its throat and either cuts its jugular veins with a bite, or strangles it.

After a strenuous chase it may be a few minutes before the cheetah regains its breath, but while it is doing so, it keeps watch all the time in case lions or hyaenas have witnessed the hunt and are coming to rob it of its meal. Eating is a messy business as the best strategy is to tear the carcase to pieces and swallow as much and as quickly as possible before other predators arrive.

Hunting success varies from one habitat to another. Clearly, it is more difficult to reach the critical distance between predator and prey when there is no cover. Young animals are usually caught, but for adults it would be something like one success out of two or three chases. There are also many abortive attempts when the prey becomes alerted before the predator gets near enough and the cheetah gives up without a chase. It would be unusual for a cheetah to kill every day.

Sociality

Cheetahs are usually solitary, but you can see them in groups. A mother and her cubs may remain together for 14–18 months, by which time the cubs are as big as she is. When the cubs become independent, they keep together for a time, but any females go off on their own before their first oestrus at 20–22 months, while the male cubs remain together longer. When you see a group of cheetah, it is usually either a mother with her cubs, sibling males, or unrelated males that have joined forces.

Territoriality

In regions like the Serengeti, several males may band together to hold a territory, but females are more solitary, have larger ranges and tend to follow the movements of their prey. Mating opportunities arise when females pass through male territories, so the latter are often located in the best hunting areas as these are more likely to be visited by females.

Males defend and mark their territories, and if a stranger wishes to pass through, it will usually try to avoid contact and pass on as quickly as possible, but fights may occur and occasionally they may be fatal. Nicked ears and scars are common signs of previous combat.

Territorial marking is an important activity. It is not unusual to see a male cheetah go up to some prominent landmark such as a tree trunk or termite mound, sniff it carefully, spray it with urine and scruff the earth with its hind feet. This action may not be a direct warning to others to keep out, but it certainly makes the intruder aware that the territory is occupied. Individuals can be recognised in this way by their personal scents.

In the Serengeti, cheetahs are concentrated in the more woody areas during the dry season as more game is to be found there than on the barren plains; but when the rains bring the gnus and gazelles back again to the short-grass areas, the cheetahs follow them, returning once more to their old ranges for the next dry season. However, a few adult cheetah, particularly the territorial males and some of the younger animals, do not follow the herds in this way.

Breeding

Although cheetahs can conceive before two years old, they seldom rear their young successfully until they have gained experience – often when 3–4 years old. The average litter is four, but seven is possible.

The mother chooses dense vegetation to have her cubs, well away from other predators. At birth, they are blind and nearly black, except for a covering of light grey fur over the back which gives them a superficial resemblance to honey badgers. Their eyes open at around 11 days, and they can walk by the time they are three weeks old.

During the day, the mother leaves them hidden, returning at night to suckle and guard them. Occasionally she may move them to a new hide-out by carrying them by the nape, one by one. The cubs have a short ruff on the nape, which persists until they are mature, so the presence of a ruff is a good way to distinguish well-grown cubs from their mother.

The cubs are very playful and most engaging to watch. When 5–6 months old, they will follow their mother during the day and watch her hunt, but when rather bigger, they may be a liability, by alerting the prey to their presence. When she kills, she may drag the carcass under a bush where the family is better concealed, or call the cubs to the carcass with staccato calls and a low whickering. The mother usually has to chew through the tough skin of the prey to make it easier for her cubs to eat, and after they have fed, will groom them, licking the blood from their faces. She occasionally purrs when with her cubs, and is the only large cat to do so.

The cubs are very vulnerable during their first three months. It is not unusual for more than 60% to die during this period from predation, disease, starvation or from grass fires – after that, there are fewer losses. If the mother loses her full litter, she will come into oestrus within three weeks and mate again.

When the cubs are older, they have to be taught to hunt and kill. They learn by watching their mother, but she also brings back live prey which is released near the cubs so that they can practise hunting techniques. However, practice over many months is necessary before they become proficient, and even when they have left their mother, they may find it difficult to kill enough for their needs.

Status

The cheetah's future is a matter of concern. The species is inevitably restricted in its distribution to certain habitats, and even there it is never common. Apart from being poached for its spotted coat, it is a diurnal hunter and its hunting forays may well be aborted by the presence of tourist buses. Getting too near cheetahs which are actively searching for prey is something that should strictly be avoided in spite of the natural desire to obtain good photographs.

Leopard

The question often asked by your friends on returning from a safari is, 'Did you see a leopard?'. There is something very special about these beautiful spotted cats, and being difficult to find, to watch one is a highlight for any tour. Heavier in build than the cheetah, a leopard personifies strength and grace. Unlike the cheetah, the spots on back and sides are in clusters and the head is larger in proportion to the body, with no 'tear' mark. A male has been known to weigh up to 81 kg, and a female, 59 kg, but most are considerably lighter. Individuals may be recognised by a combination of spot pattern on the face and ring pattern on the long, impressive tail. The white underside of the tip of the tail, shown when the mother loops her tail over her back, acts as a vivid signal to her cubs when she leads them through long grass.

The camouflage of the coat is extremely effective in many habitats, as it resembles the dappling caused by sunlight through leaves. When hiding by day, a leopard is well nigh invisible to both prey and enemies, unless it moves.

I was greatly impressed by a driver on one safari. A leopard had been seen in the early morning going into an area of thick bushes. Slowly, he combed the area, circling the bushes and eyeing the vegetation with great concentration. Nothing stirred. After some time, he gave up the search and we looked at other things. Coming back later in the day, he searched again, but still nothing. Then he saw it – a gently moving spot of white in the depths of a bush; it was the tip of a leopard's tail. On going nearer, we could just make out the wonderfully camouflaged body of a female with a small cub close beside her.

The leopard is even more of a loner than the cheetah, but its life style is that of a generalist, being able to feed on a much wider variety of prey, large and small. As its potential prey is usually scattered, it often has to range widely over the countryside to find it. Being so adaptable, it has the ability to survive in a variety of habitats and its skill in remaining unseen during the day allows it to live near human habitation, where it may vary its usual diet by taking dogs or goats.

A leopard can climb with great agility and its favourite habitats contain at least a sprinkling of mature trees, such as yellow-barked acacias, sausage trees and figs. Riverine forests are likely places to find them as these provide opportunities to lie in wait near game trails which lead to water. Montane forests also usually contain leopard, but they are not easy to see in this habitat. They also like dense scrub and dry watercourses, and may be found on kopjies and in habitats where rocky outcrops occur. The latter are greatly favoured as they provide caves and crevices for hiding away and ledges which are both good for basking and excellent as look-outs. Cubs are often born and reared in such places.

During the day, leopards are wary, shy and difficult to spot, although recently some have become habituated to vehicles and take little notice. Occasionally, you may see one draped elegantly along the branch of a large tree – the yellow-barked acacias around Seronera are famous for this, but more often, they hide in thick vegetation.

Food and hunting techniques

Leopards are opportunistic feeders, the prey items ranging from small rodents to large antelopes or zebras. Selection varies with habitat, but impala, waterbuck, reedbuck, gazelles and warthogs are high on the list of preferences. Gnu, kongoni, topi, zebra, dikdik, hare, hyrax, bat-eared fox, jackal, baboon, monkeys, spurfowl, guineafowl and bustards are also all taken when opportunities arise. The young of the larger species tend to be taken more frequently.

A leopard hunts alone and usually at night. Hunting by day is more frequent when a female has cubs and in times of scarcity. When hungry, it will take any chance that comes, day or night.

With large prey, a leopard will try to get near enough to pounce. In forests this is easier than in open country, but when the grass is long, the chances are better. It approaches stealthily, body low to the ground and eyes gazing intently ahead. If the pounce misses, it usually gives up, but when going for a young animal, it may bound after it at full speed.

On one safari, a leopard was discovered in a small sausage tree. It appeared to be fast asleep, but after some minutes, it sat up suddenly and looked intently towards a patch of longer grass. It quickly climbed down the trunk, head first, ran about ten metres, and then, crouching low, snaked its way forwards with slow, sinuous movements making use of any tussocks that gave shelter. We could still see nothing of the prey in the grass, but after what seemed like minutes, the leopard went back on its haunches and leapt. A steinbok shot straight into the air, missing the swipe of the leopard's paw by inches, and bounded away, but to our surprise, after about 15 metres, the steinbok turned round and looked straight at the leopard as if to say, 'I'm not such a fool as you think.' The leopard made no attempt to follow, but showed its frustration by marching briskly back to the tree, tail held vertically, the tip wagging furiously. It climbed the tree and went to sleep again. The leopard's hunting success with larger animals appears to be inferior to that of the cheetah, but no data has been collected for night hunts when success may be greater.

Having killed its prey, its problems are not over. In savannah, there are other predators which may have witnessed or heard the kill and may attempt to scavenge the carcase. Lions and hyaenas often succeed in doing this as a leopard has no chance against a group of animals and at their approach will flee for safety. It is not unusual for lions to kill a leopard if caught in the open. Given time, a leopard will drag its prey to a convenient tree, climb the trunk with the body in its mouth and wedge it safely between branches. Its strength is phenomenal, being able to deal in this way with prey as big as waterbuck calves and zebra foals. Safe from scavengers (lions can climb, but not as well as leopards), the leopard can feed undisturbed, with enough food perhaps for several days.

Sociality and territoriality

The only times when leopards are social are when male and female stay together for a few days for mating and when a female has cubs. At all other times they are solitary.

Leopards are territorial, each individual occupying its own range which provides it with all it needs – food, shelter and a mate. The territory may fluctuate in size from season to season and from place to place according to food availability. For females, this may vary from 12–40 km^2, but ranges may overlap. Male territories are larger and may include parts or all of several female ranges. When a female has cubs and prey is abundant, she may restrict her movements to a few square kilometres.

All leopards scent-mark special features in their territory by spraying urine. This is mixed with anal gland secretion giving it properties which allow recognition of the owner and its sexual status. Females in oestrus travel widely and spray trees and bushes in many parts of their range to alert males to their condition. Scent has the great advantage over sound of being persistent over a long period, so the territory owner is saved much energy. However, leopards reinforce scent signals by making coughing calls which sound like somebody sawing wood. Fights do occur between males at territorial boundaries, but avoidance is the general rule.

Reproduction

Oestrus lasts 6–7 days. Copulation is brief, but it may occur a number of times over a period of several days and is accompanied by snarling, caterwauling and neck biting. Leopards are promiscuous.

After a gestation of about three months, 2–3 cubs are born in thick vegetation or some rocky shelter. They weigh about 0·5 kg at birth and are blind for the first 7–10 days.

Because the female is solitary, she has to cope with the disadvantages of single-parent up-bringing. Protection is hazardous when hunting forays are extended, so leopard cubs become vulnerable to predation by lions and hyaenas. A mother does very well if she succeeds in rearing more than one cub.

For the first few days the mother and cubs remain close, and the bonds between them are strengthened by her constant attention to their needs as she suckles, cleans and warms them with her body. When stronger, the cubs start to investigate their surroundings, the scent of their refuge acting as a sign-post for return if they stray. They are suckled at intervals, especially at night.

The cubs are as playful as kittens, rolling, wrestling and playing with their mother's tail – its waving tip being an irresistible attraction. They are very demonstrative when the mother returns after a period of absence, faces are rubbed together and flanks rubbed in greeting. If danger threatens, a hiss from the mother will quieten the cubs immediately, but if disturbed while on their own, they will erect their fur, spit aggressively and defend themselves with raking movements of their claws. Jackals, baboons and eagles will all attack young cubs.

When older, they learn to climb small trees and bushes and quickly become very skilled; this is important as climbing is their best defence when threatened by hyaena or lion. They are weaned at around three months and when the mother brings back food, may squabble fiercely for possession.

Cubs first go off on their own when about 13 months old, but early on they repeatedly meet up with their mother as their hunting success is very poor at first and they rely considerably on her provision. By 18 months they are largely independent, the males, which are usually larger, tending to leave first.

Status

Because they kill domestic stock occasionally, everybody's hand is against them, and poaching for their coats is widespread. However, their ability to hide away successfully makes them difficult to kill, and in recent years in the National Parks they appear to have increased slightly. In forests, they are less vulnerable to humans and are holding their own.

Lion

Nobody mistakes a lion for anything else. The magnificent mane of the mature male attracts immediate attention – a good reason why most of the stalking is done by the smaller, less conspicuous and sleeker females. The mane, which varies in colour from tawny to nearly black, does not reach full development for four or five years, and to the casual observer an immature male may look rather like a lioness, so it is useful to look out for the early signs of a mane– the tufts of hair on forehead, neck and shoulders.

Because lions are mainly active at night, when most of the hunting is done, the visitor is fortunate to see them doing very much other than resting. However, in the early morning you may find them still feeding on a carcase, or see them making their way to water or another area, but as soon as the day hots up they retreat to any shade available. Here they stretch out and laze the day away while digesting their meal. A lion may be inactive for 20 out of the 24 hours.

Like most carnivores, lion are very curious about unusual objects that they encounter. On one occasion when we arrived at a camp in the South Luangwa National Park, we were told that lion had visited the huts the night before and investigated the washing bowls left on the tables outside. Two plastic bowls and one of aluminium had been chewed up and the lion appeared to have had a lot of fun – not so the visitors inside the very flimsy huts. It was therefore suggested that for the next night we should keep the doors of the huts fastened (string seemed to be the only means) and an oil lamp should be placed outside each hut in case the lions returned. More realistically, a ranger was to stay on guard during the night with a rifle. We slept remarkably well, but one member of the party had to get up in the night to go to the loo – a hut on the outskirts of the camp. It was a dark night, but he was just able to see a strange white object dancing up and down between him and his objective. This turned out to be the white vest of the ranger, who being black, was otherwise invisible in the poor light. He was gesticulating to warn him not to go further, because, as he soon explained, there was a lion by the loo.

Sociality

A pride ranges in number from 3–40 and usually contains mature lions and lionesses, sub-adults and cubs of various ages. The stable element within the unit is the group of adult females (up to 15) which are close relatives – mothers, sisters, daughters or cousins, and remain members of the same pride all their lives. The 1–7 mature lions are only temporary pride members, perhaps for a few months only, but sometimes for several years. Usually, they too are closely related, but not to the females. Sometimes the pride males leave voluntarily, but more often they are ejected by younger, stronger or numerically superior contenders.

You seldom see all members of the pride together at one time, and in a large pride the lionesses usually split into groups of varying composition which hunt independently. Male lions are often seen as a group apart from the lionesses; however, if the latter have made a kill they soon mix in.

Territoriality

Male and female groups have their own overlapping territorial systems; males defend their's against other males and females against other females. Territories vary enormously in size according to food availability, some being as large as 400 km^2. Sometimes a male group may overlap those of two or three female prides which are mutually antagonistic.

A stable territory for the group of females has many advantages as all parts of the area become well known. Experience builds up about successful hunting localities, useful hide-outs and observation posts, and places where cubs can be hidden and brought up successfully.

The males advertise their occupation of a territory by marking trees and bushes with a mixture of urine and scent from the anal glands, and at night especially, will roar repeatedly to warn their neighbours that they are in residence. Any intruder which trespasses too far will be chased off or fought. Lionesses also roar and mark objects in their territory with urine. If you listen to a bout of roaring you can often hear a similar response from a neighbouring pride.

Severe fighting, sometimes with fatalities, occurs when one or more nomadic males challenge the dominance of the resident lions. If successful, they will take over the role of mating, and if small cubs are present, may kill them, so that only their own genes are passed on to the next generation. The deposed lions then become nomads and have to fend for themselves.

Some lions of both sexes pursue a nomadic way of life. This has the advantage that they can follow the herds of herbivores when they migrate seasonally and so keep well fed. By contrast, the territorial prides remain in one area and suffer the privations caused by seasonal shortages. However, being a nomad has the great drawback that breeding success is very poor due to the hazards of having no stable habitat.

Food and hunting techniques

Lions can feed on large prey because of their great strength and their ability to co-operate when hunting. Their preference is for prey within the 15–1000 kg range which includes buffalo, zebra, giraffe, warthog, gnu, gazelles and all the larger antelopes. Choice is usually determined by prey abundance and ease of kill, so the old, the young and the disabled are often singled out. A pride of 20 may kill 500–600 prey animals a year.

Lion also scavenge the prey of other predators, particularly hyaena, cheetah and leopard. This is particularly evident in the Ngorongoro Crater where hyaena are much more common than lion. Here, the hyaenas do most of the hunting and killing and the lions scavenge the carcases after driving them off.

In the Serengeti, hunting success when several lions co-operate, is about one in four during the day and one in three by night; it appears to be greater on moonlight nights when their excellent sight can be utilised. A lion hunting on its own has a much poorer hunting success; about one in seven.

Lion may go for days without food, and then, after a successful hunt, make up for it by gorging themselves until almost too full to move. During the dry season when food is scarce they may have to resort to much smaller prey such as gazelles, hares, spring-hares, lizards and tortoises. They like to drink every day especially after feeding. It is a wonderful sight to see a pride of perhaps 15 or more animals drinking together at a water hole, their tawny bodies packed shoulder to shoulder, with heads lowered, lapping up the water with their long pink tongues.

When large prey is killed, it is not unusual to see ten or more animals around the carcase, bodies packed like sardines and all heads within reach of the food. There is no obvious hierarchy when feeding, although it is evident that the biggest get most and the small cubs least – with small kills, they get nothing at all. Exceptionally, large males have been seen to chase off females, allowing cubs to reach the carcase.

Hunting is done largely by the lionesses and several may co-operate. They often spend much time stalking, keeping low to the ground and using any available cover, but they take no account of wind direction; sometimes they will fan out to increase their chances. When lions know their ranges well they may attempt to trap their prey in an area such as a marsh where escape is more difficult. The stalk is followed by a rush and a pounce, and if the prey is large, one may attempt to leap on to its back. Killing is often achieved by clamping the jaws over the muzzle, causing suffocation. On one occasion a camera-man was filming a single lioness attacking a bull gnu which stood its ground and lowered its horns aggressively. The lioness retreated a few paces and rolled over on her back and the gnu stepped forwards to attack. It was a fatal move as the lioness, still on her back, was able to clamp her jaws over its muzzle and hang on until the animal fell. It appeared to be a genuine ruse for luring the gnu into a vulnerable position.

Reproduction

The pride males mate with all the females when they come into oestrus. There is no mating hierarchy, but possession is respected. Oestrus lasts 3–5 days, and during this period the couple leaves the pride. Copulation stimulates the release of eggs from the ovary and as it occurs roughly every 21 minutes over a period of several days fertilization becomes more likely, but even so, conception does not always follow.

Cubs may be born at any season. A lioness will leave the pride to have her cubs in some secluded spot; litters of two or three are most usual. A cub weighs about 1.4 kg at birth and the eyes do not open until a few days later. The cubs remain hidden in dense vegetation for about six weeks, gulleys containing bushes are favourite places, the mother returning at intervals to suckle them. However, when food is scarce, the mother often has to travel far to kill and the interval between suckling may be so long that the cubs may starve. At around 6–7 weeks, the cubs are brought back to the pride, and as it is usual for several lionesses to have cubs at about the same time, they may suck from any lioness in milk.

As many as two thirds of the cubs die, mainly from starvation, and it is a matter of luck whether cubs are born at a time of plenty or scarcity. But if a litter dies, the mother quickly comes into oestrus once more and her new cubs may have a better chance. So in lion society, cubs may be numerous, but it is the environment that determines how many survive.

CHAPTER 8

Other Carnivores of the Savannah

Many species of carnivore are mainly active at night and hide away very effectively during the day so that they are not seen so often by the visitor. However, a few species are truly diurnal and others may be seen spasmodically, especially in the early morning and late afternoon. Only these will be described in this chapter, and the more strictly nocturnal ones will be discussed in Chapter 15.

Spotted Hyaena

Popular belief has it that the spotted hyaena is a mean, dirty scavenger, an object of fear and loathing. It is true that its massive head, formidable jaws, sloping back and generally scruffy appearance do not add up to most people's idea of beauty, but in reality, hyaenas are well-adapted, efficient hunters, worthy of considerable respect.

Until researchers followed their activities at night, the sight of lions on a kill at dawn with hyaenas waiting for their turn at the carcase, gave rise to the understandable assumption that the lions had killed and the hyaenas were waiting their chance. The truth is often quite the opposite as in all probability the hyaenas had been the killers, the lions had stolen their prey and the hyaenas were waiting to finish the carcase when the lions had had their fill.

Their way of life is very flexible. They are sometimes solitary, but basically social, usually hunters, but often scavengers, and always opportunistic. The great strength of the jaws and neck muscles enables them to cope with huge weights. A single animal will easily carry away the severed head of a gnu, and even a buffalo head can be dragged across rough land to some hiding place where it can be eaten in peace. A few animals will soon dispose completely of some large herbivore; tough skin is torn apart and huge bones are crushed and eaten.

During the day, hyaenas tend to hide away in gullies and thick vegetation, emerging towards evening and hunting mainly at night. They are the most numerous predators in the Mara and Serengeti, and in the Ngorongoro Crater are far and away the dominant killers.

Sexes are extremely difficult to distinguish in the field as both males and females appear to have similar sex organs. The clitoris of the female is enlarged to look like a penis and a false scrotum is present, which in reality is just a bag of skin. No wonder that in the past, hyaenas were thought to be hermaphrodite. However, one distinguishing feature between the sexes of adults is their size, the females being larger than the males.

Sociality

Hyaenas live in large aggregations of up to 60 animals known as clans. It is a loose society where individuals or small groups can range widely, but can derive the benefits of social activities such as hunting, breeding and defending a food resource. The clan is a matriarchal society, the mature females being dominant to the males.

When members of a clan meet, they do so with a mixture of fear and aggression, as each is a potential killer and mistakes must not be made. To reduce the possible hazards, they go through elaborate greeting ceremonies which enable them to distinguish friend from foe and recognise the others' status. They sniff each others' mouths, necks and heads, then stand sideways-on and sniff the others' genitals. A cub, when approaching an adult, may make a submissive gesture by rolling on its back.

Hyaenas also communicate their moods and intentions by body language; in particular the position of the tail and ears. When undisturbed, the tail is carried straight down, when feeling aggressive, vertically upright, and when frightened, between the legs. When the ears are pointed forwards, it is a sign that it could become aggressive, if backwards, that it would like to retreat.

They also communicate with a wide range of calls. The familiar whoop is a contact signal which can be heard several kilometres away. It is repeated at intervals, and as each member of the clan has its distinctive voice, identity as well as location can be determined by this means. The most frenzied calls are the yells and maniacal cackling that occur when hyaenas become greatly excited, or when disputing a kill.

Territoriality

Territoriality is very evident when hyaenas occur in high densities, as in the Ngorongoro Crater. Here a territory may be as small as 12 km^2, but in the Mara and Serengeti they are much larger and more trespassing occurs. Within each territory there is a main den which acts as a refuge during the day, a meeting place for the clan and a safe breeding burrow system. Each territory is of sufficient size to provide ample food for the clan and is defended vigorously against strangers. If a clan is hunting a herbivore which runs on to another clan's territory, the chase may be abandoned at the boundary, but if they trespass too far, a battle royal may develop between the two clans.

A territorial boundary is regularly marked by group patrols, usually led by a female. Marking is done in several ways. There are often communal defaecating areas near a boundary which are used for this purpose. They are easily recognised by the widely-scattered white droppings – white because of the high proportion of calcium products derived from the bones eaten. Hyaenas also 'paint' grasses with a glutinous secretion from the anal glands. To do this, a strong grass stem is pulled between the legs leaving a smelly message stuck to it. They also mark the ground with secretions from glands between their toes by scraping their feet on the ground.

In places where density of prey varies with the seasons, hyaenas have much larger territories, so marking boundaries effectively becomes impossible. Marking is then limited to frequently-used routes, and trespass is tolerated much more. In such areas, large clans are less obvious as hunting activity is restricted to small groups or individuals. However, in such cases, the clans still exist and have core areas which are scent-marked and where dens are sited. Individuals, including nursing mothers, commute to where the prey concentrations are, returning every few days to the core area. Their commuting range may be as much as 70 km in a night. By so doing, hyaenas are the only predators that can effectively exploit the migratory herds of the Serengeti.

Food and hunting techniques

Hyaenas are adaptable and opportunistic in their feeding habits. Wherever animal waste is available from the kills of other animals, from animals that die by accident or disease, or where there is refuse from villages or farms, hyaenas will dispose of it. The greater the supply, the more they will scavenge and the less they will hunt. The reverse occurs when less waste is available, prey is abundant, and when numbers are high.

Hyaenas are extremely efficient feeders as they can eat and digest every part of the kill except the horns and hooves. On one occasion, a clan of 38 was seen to demolish an adult zebra in 15 minutes.

They bolt their food in large lumps and at great speed – a considerable advantage when lions are around to rob them of their kill. It is not unusual for them to gulp 14 kg of meat at a meal – perhaps a third of their own weight. In times of plenty, they may store excess food in water if there are no crocodiles about; this is a good device as there is no smell to attract other animals. They find the food again by diving and searching the area where they dumped it.

Hyaenas are very much at home in water. In Ruwenzori National Park, a hippo died of starvation in one of the pools and its body remained in the water for several days. One night, a number of hyaenas collected; some were on shore, others splashing about in the water near the dead animal. In the light from our headlights, it was extraordinary to see the dancing reflections of their eyes as they tore at the carcase. They swam very well and dived repeatedly to snatch pieces from below, coming up at intervals to breathe and gulp down great mouthfuls of rotting flesh.

Their prey is very varied and is determined largely by availability. Gnus are favourites in many areas, and when breeding, hyaenas gorge themselves on the vulnerable calves. Zebras are hunted too, and when the larger animals are scarce, gazelles are taken in large numbers. In other areas, Uganda kob and other species of antelope are important prey, particularly their young. They will also take baby hippos.

Hunting techniques differ widely according to the size of prey. A single hyaena will seldom attack large prey on its own unless it is badly injured. With zebra, a large pack will follow a family and attempt to isolate one animal, usually a foal, avoiding the attacks of the stallion which tries to defend from the rear. If separated, the pack converges on the victim and tears it to pieces. Then each fends for itself and takes as much as it can manage, carrying it off to eat in peace.

With gnus, a single hyaena may rush into the herd while the others watch for a weak, injured, or younger animal. Having made their selection, they all help in the attack. Small antelopes and the young of larger ones are attacked by a single hyaena or a pair. Some individuals learn special techniques for catching prey. For example, in the Ngorongoro Crater, a hyaena may wander nonchalantly along the shore of the soda lake where flamingoes are feeding and suddenly rush into the water to catch one before it has time to take off. Hyaenas are such effective killers, that when in large numbers, as in the Ngorongoro Crater, they control the density of the gnu population.

Reproduction

When hyaenas mate, copulation may be repeated several times. Gestation is about three months and the young, usually two, are born in dens. Several females may have their litters at around the same time, and although a mother keeps with her cubs at first, after a few weeks they live together in a creche. The cubs are nearly black at first, weigh about 1 kg and already have their eyes open.

When a mother returns from hunting, usually in early morning or late evening, she will approach an entrance near where her cubs are lying and make a purring sound. The cubs then emerge and she lies down to suckle them. No food is brought back to the den, so when food is scarce, the mother may be forced to go long distances and be away from her cubs for several days at a time. Starvation is a common cause of death during times of scarcity.

The cubs are dependent on milk alone for at least eight months, but weaning is prolonged and may span a similar period. During this time, the cubs follow the pack and get what scraps they can, but they do not join in the hunt until fully grown.

Hunting dogs

You are very fortunate if you come across a pack of wild dogs as they are here today and gone tomorrow. A pack may roam over 2,200 km^2 and are only centred on one area for a few weeks when breeding.

They look like a powerful breed of domestic dog, with black muzzle and a very variable pattern of black, yellow and white patches over the body. No individuals are alike, so the pattern allows instant recognition between pack members. The white tip to the tail is easily seen and acts as a signal. Sight appears to be their dominant sense, but smell and hearing are also well developed. The enormous rounded ears are an obvious feature.

Sociality

Hunting dogs have evolved a society which is highly organised, well disciplined and remarkably cohesive – a social order unsurpassed among the larger African carnivores. What is so remarkable about this society is that the welfare of the pack comes before that of the individual. They show mutual respect and deference to one another based on a hierarchical system, and there is no squabbling over food when prey is killed as each eats according to its status, and if there is not enough for all, the pack will attempt to kill again until all are satisfied.

Packs consist of about ten animals on average, but numbers vary considerably and may be much larger. They are permanent social groups, often with rather more males than females. Both sexes share the hunting and the upbringing of the pups.

Hierarchy occurs among both males and females, but there is little serious fighting; each seems to know its place in the system. If dominance needs to be expressed, a high-ranking dog will stand with head erect, facing the other, ears upright and tail straight down and motionless. If this threat posture needs to be accentuated, the head is lowered and the ears are projected sideways. The lower-ranking dog shows submission by lowering its head with ears laid back and the tail wagging vigorously. Food begging postures are used by the pups when the pack returns to the den with food; it involves licking the adult's lips or prostrating before it. These actions have also become ritualised to appease aggression when interactions between individuals occur at other times.

They are not territorial, but some scent marking is carried out. The dominant female will mark the den area thoroughly with urine, and all animals may mark tufts of grass in this manner when travelling. These act as sign posts, enabling those which stray to become re-united with the pack.

Food and hunting

Hunting dogs do best where there are concentrations of medium-sized herd animals. They will tackle anything from a young Tommy to a zebra, although with the larger animals, they usually select those not fully grown. They will also take smaller prey such as hares and cane rats.

The pack usually hunts twice a day, in early morning and late afternoon. Each hunt is preceded by a ritual, which has been admirably likened to that practised by a sports team before an important match to boost determination and togetherness and get the adrenalin flowing. It is usually initiated by a pack leader and involves nosing each other, licking lips, twisting and turning in a tight circle with much squeaking and whickering, the dogs becoming increasingly excited. After a short spell of this frenzied activity, they move off to look for prey.

Hunting success depends on persistence, speed and stamina. There is no attempt to hide or stalk, but the whole pack works together as a team. The usual technique is to walk slowly towards a herd, and if the animals panic, rush in to confuse and harass. The strategy is to try to isolate an individual and then pursue it relentlessly. Often, several dogs will follow on a broad front, so that if the prey swerves, it can be cut off. The chase may last for 10–60 minutes and continue for several kilometres. On a long chase, dogs from the rear which have travelled more slowly will take the place of those in front which are tired. The dogs bite repeatedly at the legs and belly of the animal until it stops, then the whole pack closes in and tears it apart. With prey as large as a zebra, a dog may leap at its muzzle and literally hang on while the others attack it. This is not a pretty sight to witness; however, it is probable that the prey is so shocked that it feels little. The flesh is bolted down in large lumps.

Reproduction

When mating occurs, it is usually the highest-ranking male that copulates with the highest-ranking female, each episode being briefer than in domestic dogs. When packs are small, it is usual for only the dominant female to breed, but there are many exceptions when two or even three females will do so.

Once a year when a female is nearly ready to give birth, the pack selects a den in a place where prey is abundant. This is often a hyaena burrow with a number of entrances. She gives birth below ground to anything up to 19 pups. However, the usual number is between 10 and 16. If a second female breeds it is hardly surprising that she keeps to another chamber.

The pups remain underground for the first three weeks, the mother guarding and suckling them. During this time, the pack brings back food for the mother who uses the begging posture to encourage regurgitation.

When the cubs first emerge above ground they keep near the entrance and retreat *en masse* if frightened or when danger threatens. As they become stronger, they are very playful and adults may join in the fun. They pull at each other's tails and that of their mother, bite playfully at ears and muzzle and tumble over each other in their excitement

The mother suckles her pups when standing upright, so with a large litter there is a furry scrummage as the mass of pups compete vigorously for her teats. Its not surprising that a suckling session lasts less than three minutes.

Weaning starts at around four weeks, the pups becoming more and more dependent on the meat brought back in the stomachs of pack members. There is a frenzied rush of pups when the adults return, and they go through the begging ritual, licking muzzles and rolling over to display their bellies. The adults regurgitate, and the cubs eagerly swallow as much as they can hold.

For the first eight months, the cubs have dominance over the adults for food, so while the cubs feed, the adults stand around and guard them from other predators. Only when the cubs are replete do the adults feed, and then, even the mother may not find it easy to get sufficient however much she begs from those who have been hunting. By eight weeks, the pups look like small adults and may make short sorties with the pack. By ten weeks, the den is abandoned and the whole pack becomes nomadic again.

Status

In recent years humans have had a devastating effect on hunting dog populations. With people hungry for land, the great wild herds are largely confined to the National Parks and hunting ranges for the dogs have become greatly restricted. In many parts of Africa dogs have been ruthlessly destroyed because of their stock-raiding reputation, although in the parks, attitudes are now more enlightened. Furthermore, with the great increase in domestic animals, the chances of infection with canine distemper has grown. There seems little doubt that this disease has been, and still is, a potent factor in restricting numbers in spite of a high reproductive potential and a social system which greatly favours the raising of pups.

Jackals

These are related to dogs. The species most likely to be seen by day are the black-backed (often called the silver-backed) and golden jackals. The side-striped is more strictly nocturnal, although it is occasionally seen in more secluded areas by day, the visitor is more likely to see one after dark in the lights from one of the lodges such as Kilaguni. It may be distinguished from other jackals by the oblique stripe on the side of the body caused by adjacent lines of white and dark hairs. All three species have rather similar life styles, but by having different habitat preferences they are usually kept apart. Nevertheless, in the Serengeti and Ngorongoro Crater you can often see both golden and black-backed at the same carcase. It is these two species that will be discussed in this chapter.

The golden jackal, which is an overall sandy colour, prefers the semi-arid short-grass plains, while the black-backed, with its striking silvery-black back and tawny sides and belly, prefers more wooded and scrubby areas. In most of the National Parks in Kenya the black-backed is more common.

Both species are crepuscular by preference, but they can be active by day or night. You may often catch sight of them around a kill in the early morning, or trotting purposefully around their territory on their own, in pairs, or as a family, usually well spread out.

Jackals have the reputation of being scavengers, but although scavenging is important, only a small proportion of their food is obtained in this way. Primarily they are opportunistic foragers with rather unspecialised habits, well adapted for exploiting a very varied diet.

Sociality and territoriality

The social unit in both species is the family, which forms a close-knit group in which the parents are paired for life. The family may be extended beyond the first litter to include yearlings of a previous one. These additional members co-operate in rearing the young by bringing back food to the lactating mother and by feeding, grooming and protecting the small cubs. This co-operation greatly improves the chances of cub survival and gives useful experience of cub rearing to the yearlings.

Hierarchy is evident between members of the social group, the helpers being submissive to the adults. Dominance is demonstrated by eye-to-eye confrontation, followed by a sudden swing of the body through 180° causing the rump to strike the side of the other.

The status and intentions of an individual are demonstrated, as in domestic dogs, by the position of the tail, lips and ears. This is supplemented by anal sniffing, which adds more information about status and sexual condition. Faeces, and in particular, urine, are both used to mark territory and den sites, and you often see a jackal stop at a marked site, sniff it carefully and sometimes reinforce the scent with its own contribution.

Jackals also communicate through a wide range of howls, yelps, barks and whines. The howl can be ear-splitting and may be heard over long distances. In the golden jackal it serves as a contact call, but it also helps to advertise that a territory is occupied. Contact calls in the black-backed are more often intermittent yelps. Although both species make the same type of sound, they differ sufficiently to avoid being misunderstood by the other.

Both species hold territories of 1–3 km^2. The owners know these areas extremely well and regularly patrol them, being ready at any time to take advantage of any food opportunity. Some jackals may become nomadic and follow the migratory herds just as lions and cheetahs do.

Food and hunting

If there is a lion or hyaena kill on or near their territory, jackals will quickly gather, usually keeping on the periphery until a chance comes to dart in, grab a piece and retreat with it. Their phenomenal agility helps them to avoid the jaws or paws of the larger predators. They will also scavenge any carcase they find, and may locate one by watching the behaviour of vultures. However, this device does not always pay off as they may occasionally be fooled by a flock of storks soaring on the thermals. When gnus are breeding, jackals will haunt the large herds and feed on the afterbirths; they also may frequent rubbish dumps and eat any refuse they can find.

As hunters, they kill a wide range of prey: invertebrates, amphibia, reptiles, birds and smaller mammals ranging in size from small rodents to adult Tommies. They are also fond of fallen fruit such as figs, berries, fungi and underground storage roots. Rodents and fruit are particularly favoured by the black-backed species as these are readily available in the habitats they prefer. By contrast, the golden jackal living out on the plains has fewer opportunities, although rodents, such as spring hares are taken frequently.

Unlike the cats, jackals snap and bite at prey rather than cling on to it. Their hunting technique varies according to prey size. For those as large as adult Tommies, co-operative hunting is necessary, usually by a pair, or when the cubs are old enough, by the family. When hunting a young gazelle which is with its mother, a pair is sufficient. The strategy is for one jackal to distract the mother while the other runs in and bites the calf. The mother is very determined, and if the calf stays with her, the battle of wits may continue for some time, but with repeated bites, the calf becomes weakened and the chance comes to grab and run off with it. At other times, jackals are solitary hunters, looking for smaller prey. In long grass they use their sensitive ears to locate rodents and then pounce, landing with the front paws close together in the manner of foxes.

Jackals also have their enemies; leopards, in particular, often kill them, and a martial eagle may swoop on a younger animal if caught in the open, killing it by grasping it in a vice-like grip with its powerful talons.

Reproduction

In the golden jackal, courtship and mating occur towards the end of the dry season (October). The pair bond is very strong and persists until the death of a partner. The pups are born after a gestation of two months, during the rains in March and April when food is plentiful. Black-backs often have their pups in the July–October period, when fruit is more abundant and rodent numbers are high.

Both species can have large litters of up to nine, but four is average. The pups are born in one of the dens on their territory and remain below ground for about three weeks. The mother stays with them most of the time, and if helpers are in attendance, is fed by them on regurgitated food. She frequently moves her pups from one den to another, carrying them hanging limply in her mouth if too young to walk. She nurses them until about two months old, and by three months, the den is abandoned. The cubs are regularly fed by regurgitation until about five months, after which they join in the hunting and feed on anything they can get hold of.

Bat-eared fox

This is a highly specialised carnivore largely dependent on insects for its food. Its enormous ears enable it to locate the movements of insects underground which are then exposed by the rapid digging actions of the fore paws. The sharp muzzle is well adapted for snapping them up.

The handsome tail which is such a conspicuous feature of these little foxes is swished violently from side to side when pursued by a predator. This is a similar device to that used by the white-tailed mongoose and serves to distract the pursuer from the vulnerable body.

Being largely crepuscular and nocturnal, the visitor is most likely to see them near their burrows in the early morning before they retire underground for the day. They may frequently be seen in the Mara, Serengeti and Ngorongoro Crater.

Their burrows (often several within their territory) are usually found where large herbivores are abundant; out on the open plains or in the woodlands. The vast amount of dung produced by the herds attracts dung beetles which are a favourite food. Certain grasses are also associated with the great herds and these are the favourite food of harvester termites which in turn are the principal food of the foxes. Harvester termites live underground during the day, but emerge in large numbers after dark to feed on the grasses. The foxes also take grasshoppers, lizards, small rodents and fruits of various kinds.

A breeding pair has 2–5 young, born underground. Occasionally, a male may share a burrow with two females. The cubs grow quickly and by four months may be as large as their parents. They may sometimes be seen together as a group, although they feed independently.

Serval

This medium-sized cat with its elegant, spotted coat has relatively long legs and enormous ears. These features are adaptations to its mode of life as a hunter in tall grass. In such a habitat, the coat gives good camouflage and the legs allow the head to be raised well above the ground, helping both sight and hearing. The ears act like radar screens for pin-pointing any sound caused by slight movements of prey.

The visitor is more likely to come across a serval by chance rather than design. They are mainly crepuscular, but the best chance of seeing one is in an area of long grass in the early morning before they shelter from the heat. Apart from savannah, they may be seen in higher alpine regions. In the Aberdares, for example, they are not uncommon, and black and intermediate forms may be encountered there.

Servals feed mainly on small mammals, including hares, rodents and the young of small antelopes, but they take birds such as spurfowl, francolin and quail and other ground-nesting or roosting species. They also feed on grasshoppers and other insects and such plant foods as fruits and grasses.

A serval's hunting technique is to travel slowly through its home range, stopping frequently to look and listen for potential prey. On locating an animal by sight, hearing or both, it stalks and leaps. In a long-grass area in Uganda, I was able to watch a serval hunting at night. Being in a Land Rover, and using a dim light, it was possible to see both the serval and the hare it was hunting. The stalk was completely silent and in ultra-slow motion. With body low, each paw was moved with the greatest care and precision. The hare was invisible to the cat, but each time the hare moved a few paces to take another nibble, the great ears, working independently, took fixes on its new position. When it got within three metres of the hare it stopped, the hare moved a step and the serval sprang high in the air in a great arc landing just short of its prey, which leapt away. Having missed, the serval made no attempt to follow, but continued its stealthy movements looking for another opportunity.

Each serval has its own home range of at least 10 km^2, but uses a core area within it much more than outlying parts. There is much overlap between serval ranges, the males wandering more widely than the females. They regularly mark certain features within their ranges by spraying with urine, often accompanied by scrapings of the hind feet. Their cheek glands are also used for rubbing against objects, as in domestic cats.

When a female has a litter, she usually chooses an area of dense vegetation; marshy areas are often chosen, but hollow trees may also be used. The 1–3 young are born blind and helpless. When she leaves them, they rely on their excellent camouflage for protection and any disturbance causes them to freeze. After about 3–4 weeks they follow their mother when she hunts, but when adolescent they are expelled from the area and have to fend for themselves.

Mongooses

These intriguing animals are related to civets and genets. There are a number of species, but the most commonly seen are the diurnal ones, in particular, the dwarf and banded mongooses. After dark at Treetops, Mountain Lodge or the Ark, you may also see white-tailed and marsh mongooses. The slender mongoose may be seen by day or night in a variety of habitats, sometimes running across the road when you are travelling through cultivated countryside. They are sleek animals with a long tail tipped with black. Very occasionally you may catch a glimpse of the great grey mongoose, which is more heavily built than the slender mongoose and occurs in bushy country. They may be seen by day, sometimes in pairs or as a family party. In this chapter only the two diurnal, social species will be considered.

Dwarf mongoose

This species occurs in packs of up to 20 individuals. They may often be seen in the vicinity of safari lodges such as Seronera, Samburu and Kilaguni, and visitors can watch their antics as they live in burrows or termite mounds within the grounds of the lodges.

When out on a game run, you may occasionally see one bolt for a termite mound and disappear down one of the holes. If this happens, it is often very rewarding to stop and wait without getting too close. Being very inquisitive, a small head is likely to appear at one of the entrances to assess the position, and if there is no movement to cause worry, it will not be long before others emerge. Their activities are most entertaining to watch as they are incredibly alert and agile as they wrestle, play and chase each other in and out of holes.

Dwarf mongooses have evolved a remarkably sophisticated social system. Each pack has a dominant pair which usually comprises the oldest male and female in the group. This pair is responsible for all the breeding activities of the pack, and if other females should become pregnant their progeny are unlikely to survive. The dominant female may keep her position for several years, so there may be a long waiting period before another female gets her chance to breed.

The pack includes adults and juveniles. The former may have been born within the group or joined it from other packs. It is not unusual for a young adult to go off and try to gain acceptance by another group. If this does not contain many older animals of the same sex, its chances of becoming a dominant more quickly are improved. This emigration to other groups lessens the chances of inbreeding and allows small groups to become bigger and therefore better able to defend themselves. As co-operation is so vital in dwarf mongoose so-ciety, large groups are more likely to survive than small.

Their main food is invertebrates such as beetles, termites and mil-lipedes, although they will occasionally take small vertebrates such as lizards. They hunt for food individually although they keep within hearing distance of each other when foraging.

Being vulnerable to attack from eagles and the smaller carnivores a good look-out has to be kept. Living in a group, they are able to co-operate in this essential task, so while most of the pack is foraging, others climb on termite mounds or tree stumps to view the sky for eagles and the countryside for other predators. The dominant male plays a major part in guard duty and if danger is detected, makes urgent alarm calls which cause the others to flee for the shelter of a termite mound or thick vegetation.

The pack repeatedly moves home, but will remain much longer in one place when breeding occurs. When the dominant female has a litter, the young are cared for by other members of the pack, and when the pack goes out foraging, baby-sitters of either sex remain behind to look after them, those on duty being relieved periodically so that all can feed. If home moving has to occur before the young can travel, they may be carried hanging limply in the mouth of an adult.

Packs move from location to location within a definite home range, but it is not unusual for another pack to trespass briefly when foraging. They use anal gland secretion to mark ground near their mounds and any prominent feature such as a tree trunk within the range. Sometimes, they make hand-stands to reach a particularly desirable prominence on which to leave their mark. Such marking is a means of telling others their individuality, sex, and probably their status.

Banded mongoose

This species is commonly seen in many of the parks. It is larger than the dwarf and has characteristic transverse bands across the back. When travelling, they seem to snake through the grass, often head to tail in a long line, but when foraging, they spread out, each hunting independently.

Packs of 40 have been known, but the usual number is between 10 and 25, which includes adults, juveniles and young. They live in dens, usually old termite mounds, but may use excavations in gullies or man-made structures.

They are diurnal, and when they emerge in the morning, they like to warm themselves in the sun before moving off as a pack to forage. In the late afternoon, or occasionally soon after dark, they return to the den area where they relax and groom, and where the young may play if not too tired. But as soon as the light begins to fade, some move towards an entrance where they form a cluster, as if loath to retire for the night; then one by one they make their way inside. They are well protected from predators, remaining tightly huddled together within the confines of the central chamber of the mound. If an occupied den is approached quietly at night, you can hear low murmurings inside and smell the warm, musky odour which emanates from the entrances. It is surprising how many animals can shelter together in such a limited space.

A pack may change its den frequently, but when breeding occurs, a den, if undisturbed, may be used for as long as two months. A den occupied for some time can be recognised by its pungent musky smell, due to constant marking by anal gland secretion and the concentration of dried droppings nearby.

They are opportunistic feeders, concentrating largely on a wide range of invertebrates, of which beetles are the most important. Termites, grasshoppers, millipedes and molluscs are also taken and small vertebrates such as lizards and toads are occasionally eaten. In Ruwenzori National Park it was evident that the packs followed the game trails of elephant and buffalo as their dung attracted many beetles and large millipedes. The mongooses would tear the dung to pieces with their front paws and pick out the prey with their mouths. They would also dig up and open the dung balls which had previously been laboriously trundled along and buried by large scarabs; the developing larvae within are a favourite delicacy.

When the pack is on the move or foraging, each member emits a constant stream of low contact calls, easily heard by others in the pack, but not loud enough to attract unwanted attention. They are constantly alert for danger, and anything unusual will cause them to stand bolt upright to get a better view. When travelling in long grass they will use any prominence as a scanning post.

If an enemy such as an eagle, is sighted, there is an explosion of alarm calls and all dive for cover. If caught in the open, they bunch together to form a compact mass of furry bodies, mouths open and pointing menacingly towards the aggressor. This probably gives the impression of a single, much larger animal, and is often enough to frighten off the attacker.

A martial eagle sometimes attempts to catch a mongoose by waiting near a den in the late afternoon for the pack to return. This happened on one occasion near Seronera when a safari group was returning from a game run. Suddenly, a martial eagle hurtled out of the sky, so near to the vehicle that its huge and powerful wings struck against a side window. The mongoose it was attempting to catch shot under the minibus just in time and into the mound on the other side. The attack was so sudden, it was quite frightening to see this enormous bird, beak open and talons outstretched, within a few feet of where one was sitting.

Jon Rood relates how a martial eagle seized an adult banded mongoose and carried it to the fork of a tree. The pack at once clustered around the tree and several bandeds started to climb, the dominant male in the lead. On reaching the struggling mongoose, the male lunged at the eagle which lost its grip and the mongoose fell to the ground unhurt. This is not the only sighting of a rescue attempt made by a mongoose pack; this time a successful one.

Their social life has many similarities to that of dwarf mongooses, but breeding is not confined to the dominant female. Although litters may be born throughout the year, it is usual for births to be synchronised, perhaps three females having families within a few days of each other. When the pack goes foraging, one or more adults of either sex remain and act as baby-sitters. On returning, the young eagerly greet the lactating females, but the young are not necessarily fed by their own mother, but go from one to another according to opportunity.

If the pack changes dens when very young animals are present, they may be carried by mouth. But sometimes you see a pack with young which start the journey on foot, but soon get tired. Presumably there is some cry for help, as the nearest adult then picks up the youngster in its mouth and carries it a short way before putting it down and giving it another run.

The banded mongoose is a very successful species, well adapted as a diurnal, mainly insectivorous carnivore. Hunting by pack seems to be a diurnal adaptation which allows each individual to exploit a widely-spread food resource, but at the same time be protected by the presence of the others and the pack's enhanced alertness. Their reproductive behaviour is also characteristic of a sophisticated social life where there is much co-operation between individuals.

We have seen in this chapter how a great variety of carnivores can live together, each with its distinctive structure, mode of life and behaviour which allows it to occupy its specific niche in the savannah ecosystem.

CHAPTER 9

Birds of the Savannah

In previous chapters we have seen how the many mammalian species present in savannah share out the food using their own specialised ways of obtaining it, and by diversifying, are able to reduce competition. A similar picture emerges for the birds.

Bird species are very numerous and one of the delights of a safari is quietly to observe the various kinds, marvelling at their aerial acrobatics, their colours and their great variety of form and behaviour. Field guides for their identification are essential for the bird-watcher, but to understand, even in a limited way, how the various species fit into the ecological jigsaw is an additional pleasure.

In this chapter we will first consider what food is available to the birds and then describe how each resource is exploited so that the bounty is shared between them. A few species of particular interest will be treated in more detail.

Imagine you are a bird and the savannah is your super-store. What is available on the shelves? First, the vegetation itself provides a variety of products according to species and season. Of these, fruits and seeds are of the greatest importance as they contain all the food necessary for the growth of a new plant until it can photosynthesise for itself. What is more, the food is concentrated and conveniently packaged, so they are easily dealt with given the right-shaped bill. The grasses alone provide enormous quantities of seed, which when ripened and shed, may remain wholesome for many weeks and need

101

only to be searched for. Trees which produce berries and others, like the fig, provide bumper crops of succulent fruits which attract many species. In exchange for the food provided, the birds help the trees by dispersing their seeds. The seeds of succulent fruits often have very hard coats which can withstand being digested in the bird's gut, but become sufficiently softened to allow germination when voided with the droppings. As this can occur some distance from the parent tree, competition for living space between members of the same species is reduced.

Nectar and pollen are exploited more by insects than birds, but sunbirds are able to harvest the nectar using their fine curved bills to probe the tubular flowers. Leaves can also be very nutritious, especially when young and tender, but in some species they later acquire tannins which make them bad-tasting and indigestible. So it is the bursting buds and young shoots of trees and bushes and the leaves of such herbaceous plants as clovers that are mainly utilised. Below ground, roots and rhizomes may contain stored food and water and these can be obtained by some birds if they have the specialised equipment for dealing with them.

Although plant products are essential for many birds, it is the fauna that supplies the greatest diversity of food items. Top of the list come the insects, which occur in great numbers and in a range of sizes suitable for many kinds of birds.

Insects are found in a great variety of habitats, so different bird species have become adapted for finding them wherever they may be. Some insects, such as caterpillars and bugs, are found on the leaves of trees and bushes and are sought after by the smaller and more acrobatic birds. Others such as beetle larvae, may be found under the bark or buried in the wood itself where specialist techniques are necessary for their extraction. Locusts and grasshoppers can sometimes be found in abundance, mainly among grasses, while termites live in the soil and usually have to be probed for, so a long bill is needed. Insects may also be found in the dung of the large herbivores. Here dung beetles and flies lay their eggs and the resulting grubs are important prey for some birds. Finally, the air above the savannah contains numbers of flying insects, particularly at certain seasons, and birds such as swallows and swifts are well adapted for catching them when on the wing.

Other invertebrates which are potential bird food include molluscs, spiders, centipedes and millipedes. These can be discovered amongst the leaves and grasses or in rotting dung.

Reptiles, birds and the smaller mammals are the main food of predatory birds, prey size largely determining what species can tackle them. Carrion is the main food of such scavengers as vultures.

So in our savannah super-store there is tremendous scope for birds to exploit the many types of food available. Each species has its niche, either as a specialist which concentrates mainly on one type of food and uses its own particular techniques for obtaining it, or as a generalist which keeps its options open, can feed on a number of food sources according to availability and uses rather less specialised methods in the process. Although very few specialists strictly confine themselves to one kind of food, it is for their main preferences that they are specially adapted by having suitable anatomical features and appropriate modes of behaviour.

I will now describe the main groups of savannah birds according to their food preferences, selecting for more detailed treatment certain kinds which are commonly seen and are of particular interest.

Those which are mainly vegetarian, but also take some insects

Vegetarians vary greatly in size, ranging from the miniature sunbirds to the largest bird in the world, the ostrich. All, to varying degrees, supplement their diet with insects and other animal prey.

Nectar feeders

SUNBIRDS are primarily nectar feeders, although some will also take small insects and spiders. The visitor will find sunbirds around the safari lodges, where the tubular flowers of such trees as Erythrina and Jacaranda supply much nectar, but they also occur in savannah. So look out for concentrations of such plants as *Leonotis* (lion's ear), with its tall stems ringed with successive whorls of tubular, orange-red flowers, and the spikey-leaved aloes which are also favoured.

Sunbirds prefer to perch on or near the flower they are feeding from, sometimes clinging to it upside down to reach the nectar, but they can also hover like humming birds. If the tube is too long to reach the nectar, they may pierce the base of the tube with their slender curved bills and get at the nectar that way. However, by using this technique they fail to pollinate the flower.

Male sunbirds are vividly coloured and are wonderfully iridescent in sunshine, but the females are duller and much more difficult to identify. Their tiny hanging nests are miracles of construction, built

103

of fine plant fibres woven together, or bound with spiders' webs. They are softly lined with down feathers.

Vegetarians with a very varied diet

The OSTRICH is by far the best known, so it will be treated in more detail. It is the largest bird existing today, standing over 2 m in height and weighing 100–150 kg. It is also the only flightless bird in Africa. It makes up for its inability to fly by being able to run extremely fast – over 60 k.p.h. This enables it to outrun any predator but the cheetah.

Ostriches have strong limbs bearing only two toes, one pointing forwards and the other backwards; a kick can inflict considerable damage on any animal that dares to attack it. The male ostrich is black and white, and the females and juveniles, brown. The visitor to East Africa may see two sub-species, the Somali ostrich found in northern Kenya, including Meru and Samburu, and the Maasai sub-species in Nairobi National Park, the Mara and in many parts of Tanzania. They differ when in breeding condition by having neck and thighs bluish in the Somali, and pink in the Maasai.

They are mainly vegetarian, but are selective feeders, choosing flowers, nutritious leaves, seeds and fruits such as berries and fallen figs; occasionally they will eat small lizards and larger insects. They habitually swallow small stones to help crush the food when in the gizzard.

Ostriches are often seen singly or in small groups, but occasionally in much larger numbers. At the breeding season mature males will leave the group and set up territories which may be very extensive. A male will defend his territory with threat posturing which involves wing flapping with mouth wide open to display the red gape; if this fails to deter, fights may occur. The males also boom loudly to proclaim ownership of a territory and to entice females on to their land.

Courtship is fascinating to watch. On one occasion at Samburu, a male was seen semaphoring with wings outstretched and rhythmically swaying from side to side, but no female could be seen. However, his eyesight from two metres up was better than ours, and before long we saw a female running towards the dancing male. When she got to within a few yards of her suitor, she stopped running and also started to display. Each bird with wings outstretched dipped first one wing then the other in a remarkable ballet. The dance then became more frenzied and when their wings touched she squatted on the ground and he mounted her, wings still extended and with

104

neck greatly inflated. While mating was taking place, a second female approached and started to display in front of the pair. Ostriches are polygamous and a male will mate with three or four females which have been attracted on to his territory.

The male makes a shallow scrape in the soil to serve as a nest and each female lays her 10–15 eggs in the one nest in the course of about a fortnight. So a nest can contain more than 50 eggs, each with the capacity of about two dozen hen's eggs.

The eggs are spherical with very hard, white shells which even a lion may fail to crack. Hyaenas sometimes succeed, but it is the Egyptian vulture that manages best by picking up a large stone in its beak and hurling it repeatedly at the egg until it breaks.

As the male is more conspicuous, he usually takes the night shift when brooding the eggs, while the dominant hen takes over during daylight hours. After 5–6 weeks the chicks peck their way out of the eggs. It is not certain how they manage to do this, but it is possible that the shell softens just prior to hatching. In a large clutch a majority of eggs never hatch. A freshly emerged chick can quickly stand and soon starts pecking for food, but 25% of its weight is yolk, and this sees it through the first few difficult days.

The young are vulnerable to mammalian predators and eagles, and are protected by the male and dominant female. When travelling, one bird will often go in front while the other guards the rear. By four weeks, the chicks are able to run at 45 k.p.h., and if attacked, will rush in all directions for cover. Their camouflage is so good, that in some habitats they appear to disappear completely when they squat and freeze.

Family groups range widely, and if they meet other parties, the young mingle and the dominant pair of adults takes over all the chicks. This process may be repeated until very large aggregations are formed. The record must go to a party of 285, counted by a game warden near Isiolo in 1972. The two adults in charge must have been good disciplinarians.

The seed-eaters

Birds which are predominantly seed-eaters are usually small, with rather short, but strong, pointed bills, suitable for pecking up and sometimes crushing the hard seeds. Many species form flocks, particularly when not breeding. Considering the abundance of grass seeds in savannah, it is not surprising that there are many species which exploit this source of food; they include sparrows, true weavers, social weavers, buffalo weavers, queleas, whydahs and widow-birds.

The **RED-BILLED QUELEA** is probably the most numerous bird in the world. They are tiny and sparrow-like, less than 13 cm long and weighing about 18 g with a reddish bill and legs; when breeding, the male has a black face and suffusions of pink on head and breast. They occur in large flocks and may be seen in many habitats, including dry, bushy savannah.

From a distance a flock looks like a small cloud which constantly changes shape and direction. Suddenly, as if by command, the formation breaks up and the birds settle on leafless trees and shrubs, clothing the branches with greyish-brown 'foliage' as they fill up every available space. A brief rest, and off they go again in another aerobatic display, each bird having just enough air space to prevent wing contact.

When feeding, they drop to the ground like locusts, searching for seeds with quick, eager movements, not staying still for a moment, and repeatedly taking to the air to settle in a different place. They may be seen in concentrations of over a million birds, although in most of the national parks the flocks are much smaller. They are great migrants, and in times of drought, may leave the dry thornbush country they prefer, and raid any area where seed is abundant, including farmland.

Queleas nest in thick acacia bushes, sometimes as many as several hundred in a single large bush. A breeding colony has been known to occupy 10 km^2. They breed towards the end of the rains when the grass seeds are still soft enough for the young to digest. Many birds of prey and marabou storks gather at these breeding sites and glut themselves on eggs and chicks, but like the gnus, which also synchronise their breeding, there are always plenty that survive.

If they raid farms where wheat and millet are grown they can do colossal damage. War is waged on their breeding sites using contact poisons, sprays and even flame throwers. Millions have been destroyed in this way, but still they survive.

The **TRUE WEAVERS** are also seed-eaters although insects form part of their diet. There are many species of these birds, a number of which occur around safari lodges. The males usually have much yellow (occasionally red) in their plumage although the females and immatures are more like sparrows. Most species are communal nesters and opportunistic in their choice of when to breed. A heavy rain shower will stimulate the males to feverish activity; new nests will be made and incomplete ones finished.

106

The nest starts with a tightly-woven ring which is then enlarged to become globular; some species add a funnel-shaped entrance. Dry grasses are used most commonly by savannah weavers, although when available, they will use long strippings of banana or palm leaves which are carried in the bill and look like long streamers. Each piece is poked into place by the bill, drawn through and woven in and out with remarkable skill. If you pick up a fallen nest, you can only marvel at its intricate construction.

To make entry more difficult for predators such as snakes, the nests are suspended, usually near the end of a branch and when possible, over water. Those with funnel-like entrances are particularly well protected. There are other kinds of weavers which also make their nests communally, but their nests are not so beautifully woven as those of the true weavers.

BUFFALO WEAVERS are very common in some of the eastern and more northern parks; they make large, untidy, domed nests made of thorny twigs; a tree may have ten or more of them, some adjoining. Each nest may have two or three chambers occupied by different pairs, the entrances facing outwards, but in different directions.

The **WHITE-BROWED SPARROW WEAVER** is commonly seen around many of the lodges; it makes a bulky untidy nest of dried grass with pieces sticking out in every direction – very much in the beginner's class when compared with the nests of true weavers. **SOCIAL WEAVERS** on the other hand, make nests which are clumped together to form a massive structure with many entrances, rather like a block of flats.

WIDOW BIRDS are other seed-eaters which excite attention when in breeding condition. Jackson's widow bird is usually the most common widow bird seen in long-grass savannah. For most of the year they are insignificant, well-camouflaged, sparrow-like birds, but for a few short weeks, the male is majestically clothed in glossy black with brown shoulders and a magnificent thick, black, curved tail. At the breeding season you may come across a number of these flamboyant males spread out over a wide area and repeatedly leaping a few feet above the grass with fluttering wings and waving tail in vivid display. Through this activity each male forms a flattened area four or five feet in diameter leaving a tuft of untrampled grass in the centre. Flocks of females in the vicinity are attracted to the area by the sight of the dancing males, and if one alights within the ring, mating will take place. The male is polygamous, and may mate with five or more females, which later nest among the vegetation in various parts of his territory.

Generalists

These birds take a great variety of plant and animal food according to availability. The larger ones are ground feeders and characteristically have long necks; they include bustard, guineafowl and spurfowl. During the course of their evolution, they came to rely more on running than flight, and their legs became longer and stronger, but this took their food source further from their mouths so the neck elongated to compensate.

BUSTARDS are the largest of these generalists, large enough to be safe from the smaller predators, but able to run swiftly, or fly as a last resort, if there is danger from a larger one.

The biggest is the kori bustard. The male may weigh up to 12 kg and is the heaviest bird in Africa capable of flight; the females are considerably smaller. You see the birds strutting purposefully among the grasses searching for both plant and animal food items. The strong bill is capable of tackling prey as large as lizards and small mammals, as well as picking up seeds, pecking at leaves and snapping up insects as large as locusts. During courtship, the male stands very upright, inflates his neck so that the white feathers are erected like a ruff, and then raises his white tail over his back in a very impressive display.

GUINEAFOWL are plump, colourful, gamebirds which are not as large as bustards. They are preyed upon by many predators, but get some protection by living in flocks of 20–150 strong, where their collective alertness gives them early warning of danger. At night they fly up into favourite trees which may be recognised by day by the carpet of droppings below.

The helmeted guineafowl, typically found in woody savannah, have a bony horn protruding from the crown. They always appear to be fussily busy; continuously searching for food, scratching at the soil for termites and other insects and pecking up any seeds they can find. They have been delightfully likened to animated tea-cosies.

The vulturine guineafowl, found in more northern, arid country such as Samburu, is a very handsome bird with a striking blue iridescence when the sun shines on the neck and breast feathers. The upper neck, bare of feathers, and the relatively small head give it the vulture-like appearance that gives rise to its name.

Just before the rains, guineafowl split up and become territorial, ready for breeding. But how do they anticipate such a change in the weather? It is known that they can detect infra-sound of very low frequency, and this is capable of travelling vast distances. Thunder gives off such ultra-sounds as well as those audible to us; so it is likely that they can hear thunder many hundreds of kilometres away and anticipate the rains well before they arrive.

SPURFOWL are allied to pheasants, but lack the long tail. Unlike guineafowl, you find them singly or in pairs. Both sexes are well camouflaged and rely on concealment as their first line of defence, but if frightened, will fly fast and straight letting out an explosive volley of harsh sounds. They eat a wide variety of plant and animal food, scratching for roots and bulbs, searching for seeds and berries, pecking at tender leaves and hunting for insects such as termites, beetles and the larvae of moths and flies.

The nest is usually sited under a thick bush, and when the young hatch, they are in an advanced state, being able to follow the mother when she searches for food. The young birds, if they survive, soon pass the very vulnerable flightless stage and are quickly able to roost in trees like their parents.

Those feeding mainly on insects.

Because insects are so numerous in savannah and occur in so many different habitats, there are many niches for insectivorous birds. Competition between them is reduced by various devices, not least by their different hunting techniques; so for our purpose it is convenient to group them in this way.

Those which hunt for insects in foliage

These include the WARBLERS – those little brown birds which are often so difficult to identify. Not all are brownish, but most are sombre with pale, sometimes yellowish undersides. These colours make them difficult to see among the dappled foliage. They are all small agile birds with thin pointed bills. Their excellent eyesight enables them to pick out objects as small as insect eggs, but their main foods are small insects and spiders.

Those which hunt for insects from vantage points

Because of this habit of viewing an area for potential prey from some vantage point, these birds attract attention. Moreover, some of them are among the most beautiful birds in Africa, the rollers and bee-eaters. Although this habit is widespread, there is variation in the techniques employed by the different species.

The **LILAC BREASTED ROLLER** has a tawny brown back, lilac throat and breast, greenish-blue belly and blue tail with streamers. It may be readily approached as it sits motionless on the top of a bush or dead branch from which it can scan the ground vegetation in all directions for insects such as grasshoppers. On seeing a movement, it will sweep from its perch, displaying the gorgeous cobalt blue of its wing feathers, and pounce on its prey. If it misses, it will quickly hop after it and if successful, tear it to pieces with its strong, slightly curved bill. The roller gets its name from its display flight when it somersaults and rolls in the air in a most spectacular manner.

BEE-EATERS have a different hunting technique. For example, a pair of little bee-eaters – small green birds with yellow throats and black eye stripes – will occupy a small area where there is a selection of low bushes which act as vantage points. Unlike rollers, they look for flying insects, including bees and wasps. If an insect comes within range, the bird will quickly swoop on it, catching it in the air with an audible snap of the bill. A pair will often share the same vantage point. As with rollers, some species will use telegraph wires as lookouts. Bee-eaters are beautifully adapted for catching insects on the wing, having excellent eyesight, long pointed wings for fast erratic movements and a rather long, laterally compressed, pointed bill for snapping at prey.

FLYCATCHERS hunt in the same general manner, catching insects in flight by making short sallies when they come within range of their vantage point. However, they tackle smaller insects than bee-eaters and prefer to hunt in more shady situations. If larger prey are captured, they will bring them back to the perch, holding them down with a foot while dismembering them. You often see species such as the grey and chin-spot flycatchers in grounds of safari lodges, and occasionally, the paradise flycatcher as well.

SHRIKES are bold, aggressive birds which also hunt from vantage points; there are many species. When travelling through grassy and cultivated areas you often see fiscal shrikes on the telephone wires, each vigilant for insect movement, either in the air, or on the ground below.

The long-tailed fiscal has contrasting black above and white below with a white wing bar. It is commonly seen in bushy acacia savannah, sometimes in small parties. All shrikes have strong hooked bills, some being able to take young birds, lizards and small mammals as well as insects. Prey, too large to transport in the bill, is carried in the sharp talons. Some impale their prey on the thorns of a favourite bush to form a 'larder'. This can help when dismembering prey, but may also act as a reserve store. Shrikes are very noisy birds, their name being derived from 'shriek', but not all their cries are harsh, some being clear and melodious.

Those which hunt in ground vegetation

This group includes the closely related larks, pipits, longclaws and wagtails. LARKS and PIPITS are easily confused as they are all small to medium, brownish birds, but the latter are slimmer, more upright in bearing and have more slender bills. One of the most common savannah pipits is Richard's pipit, which can be recognised by its white outer tail feathers when it flies. Longclaws are more colourful, with throat and breast either bright yellow or pink according to species and with a black collar. They stand very upright and have particularly long claws. Wagtails have longer tails which are constantly in movement. All these species are ground feeders, walking and running as they search for flies, small beetles, grasshoppers, termites and other small invertebrates; larks, in particular, also take seeds. Some wagtails are only found near water, but races of the yellow or blue-headed wagtails, which are winter visitors from Europe, may often be seen among herd animals catching insects disturbed by their movement.

PLOVERS are also ground feeders, the commonest species seen on the open plains being the crowned plover – so called because of the white ring on its black head. It can run fast, and if disturbed, takes to the air with flapping wings and raucous cries, alerting other animals to possible danger. Nearer water, the blacksmith plover is the commonest species in many areas; it makes repeated metallic calls like that of hammer on anvil; hence the name. The crowned plover often take termites and may sometimes be observed patting the ground repeatedly with one foot whilst listening carefully for any sound made by the disturbed insects just below the surface.

Those which hunt in air

Insects fly to get from one food source to another, to find mates and to disperse. Young spiders are also wind-blown on threads of silk when dispersing. At some seasons and during certain weather conditions, astronomical numbers may be in the air at one time, especially when ants and termites are swarming, mosquitoes and midges hatching, and butterflies migrating. At these times of abundance many birds will exploit the harvest, but in times of relative scarcity only the specialists, equipped for aerial hunting, will find enough.

SWIFTS are the most aerial of all birds. They are distinguished from swallows and martins by their long, sickle-shaped wings. During daylight hours, they are in constant flight, and some species even sleep on the wing at night. Swifts do not perch, but some cling to rocky ledges when roosting, using all four forward-projecting toes to hook on tightly. They are beautifully streamlined with short necks, slim bodies and short, usually forked tails. They have marvellous eyesight, capable of locating insects with pin-point accuracy when flying at speed and then sweeping them up in their wide-gaped mouths. Swifts are so specialised for aerial conditions that they even drink and bathe when on the wing by swooping down to water; they also copulate in the air, and when nest building, collect wind-borne material.

The little swift, which has a square tail and white rump is commonly seen; it often nests communally around safari lodges. Large numbers of nests of straw and feathers may be clumped together and glued to some beam or overhang with saliva. In the absence of suitable buildings they nest under cave roofs and rocky overhangs. The glue-like saliva is also used by the palm swift to attach its egg to the open nest which it builds on the inner side of a palm leaf. The bird has to brood nearly vertically. You often see these birds flying around groups of palm trees.

SWALLOWS and **MARTINS** are not closely related to swifts, but have acquired their streamlining and rather similar appearance in response to similar needs and conditions; they have more angular wings than swifts and fly with more twists and turns. Their beaks are short, and can gape very wide to help catch flying insects. Unlike swifts, they often perch, and during rests between flights, you sometimes see bushes or small trees crowded with them, but they seldom settle on the ground except to obtain mud for their nests – made of a mixture of mud and saliva which sets very hard.

Between October and May large flocks of migrating swallows from Europe may be seen in East Africa weaving among the herbivores in their hundreds and picking off insects disturbed by their movements.

On one unforgettable occasion in Ruwenzori National Park, we saw what appeared to be three columns of smoke rising from the water of the lake, quite far out. This turned out to be a great hatch of lake flies. Later in the day, wind currents brought them to the lake shore and they were all around us in their billions. Then we saw the martins. At first there were just a few, then the numbers increased and in a few minutes they were everywhere. There were thousands and thousands of martins hawking the flies in all directions. How they managed to avoid collision seemed miraculous as they gave a fantastic display of aerobatics all around us. Wherever you looked the sky was full of martins. But when the light began to go there was a subtle change in behaviour; instead of flying in a random manner, the majority began to move more in a westerly direction, presumably towards a roosting place before it got dark. The numbers began to thin out, and soon became reduced to isolated groups, 'hedge-hopping' like starlings in Europe returning to their roosts. It was an astonishing sight to have witnessed.

Those which hunt for insects in wood and under bark

Few birds can cope with the problem of finding and extracting insect larvae in such well-protected situations, but woodpeckers are specialists in the art. Species found in woody savannah include the cardinal and nubian woodpeckers. They not only drill for insects, but take them from the bark surface, particularly ants and termites; they also supplement their diet with fruit and nuts. Their leisurely, undulating flight when flying from tree to tree is characteristic, and when they settle they explore the trunks and boughs with jerky movements, gripping the bark with their sharp claws; when in a vertical position, they use their stiff tail feathers as a prop. The strong pointed bill is a splendid tool for boring into wood, both for finding grubs and making nesting holes. Further adaptations will be mentioned when describing forest species.

Birds of prey (raptors)

Predatory birds are well represented in the savannah ecosystem as there is a wide variety of prey to exploit, ranging from mammals as large as monkeys and small antelopes to small rodents, and birds as big as hornbills or gamebirds to the smallest seed-eaters. Some will even take insects.

Factors that help to reduce competition for prey between the species include the size and strength of the raptor, as these determine the kind of prey that can be tackled. The huge martial eagle with a wing span of two metres, massive hooked bill and immensely strong talons, is able to kill small antelopes; but the pygmy falcon, not much bigger than a sparrow and weighing a mere 70 g, only preys on insects.

Another factor which helps reduce competition is the variation in prey selection between species. Although raptors may take many species opportunistically, they have their preferences and are often specially adapted in structure and behaviour to capture them. Thus, Verreaux's eagle, that huge black eagle, showing white in its wings when it flies, specialises in killing hyraxes. It flies close to cliffs and kopjes, surprising the animals as they sun themselves on the rocks in early morning or late afternoon. Bateleurs, commonly seen soaring over the savannah with hardly a wing beat, may be recognised by their short neck and tail; they take both mammals and birds according to opportunity. By contrast, the black-shouldered kite specialises in rodents. This is a pale grey bird with white below which is commonly seen quartering grassy areas with leisurely, erratic flight, sometimes hovering briefly before it pounces.

A further means of separation is to use different hunting techniques. Peregrines, for example, swoop on their prey at great speed and strike them with their talons. Other species will sit motionless on tree-top or bough and swoop down on any prey that comes near. The chanting goshawks will do this for lizards and small snakes, and the pygmy falcon for insects. By contrast the hobby will pursue its prey on the wing, and being such a fast flier is even able to take swallows and martins. Montagu's and pallid harriers on the other hand quarter the ground with slow, low-level flight and rely on surprise to catch rodents and small birds. Kestrels prefer to hover as they scan the vegetation below, mainly for rodents.

The secretary bird hunts on foot killing snakes or lizards by striking them with repeated blows of its powerful feet. If a snake strikes back, the blow is usually taken harmlessly on the wing feathers, as the wings are kept outstretched when attacking. They will also take eggs and young birds, small tortoises, termites and locusts, and will frequently hunt for fugitives from fires along with storks of various species.

Another bird that hunts on foot is the ground hornbill. You usually see them in small parties with individuals well spread out as they search for rodents, small reptiles, frogs and a variety of insects. They are very striking birds resembling large black turkeys with red on head and throat.

Finally there are those, which, like some of the predatory mammals, drive other birds off their prey and scavenge the carcase. Tawny eagles, in particular, practice this piracy, although they will also catch prey themselves.

Further selection is achieved by hunting at night when there is less competition. Owls are splendidly adapted for a nocturnal mode of life. They have binocular vision, and their sight is remarkably good under conditions of low light intensity; however, it is their hearing that is so remarkable. This is so acute that they can pin-point the position of prey in darkness when it makes the slightest sound. This ability is helped by the position of the ears which are placed at slightly different levels on the left and right sides of the head. This helps the owl get a three dimensional fix on its prey's position.

They have also developed powers of silent flight by having all their feathers soft and downy and the flight feathers equipped with fringes on their trailing edges and on the leading edge of the first primary. Also by having broad wings, the ratio of surface area to weight of body is increased so they can fly very slowly with leisurely wing beats. Silent flight has the advantage of surprise when hunting and allows the owl to listen for any sign of movement without disturbance from the sound of its own flying.

Vultures will be considered in the chapter on scavengers.

CHAPTER 10

Scavengers

Scavengers on animal material

Animals die from many causes; predation, disease, starvation, natural disasters and old age all take their toll. Death may come at any time so there is a continuous supply of carrion throughout the seasons, although quantities fluctuate considerably with climatic extremes and disease epidemics. When it is a hard time for predators and herbivores it is a time of plenty for the scavengers.

When a large animal dies, a lot of nutritious food suddenly becomes available for any scavenger that can find it quickly enough. But carcases occur relatively infrequently and may be well spaced out over the countryside. So a good scavenger is one that has the means to range widely in search of such bonanzas, has excellent senses to lead it quickly to the carcase, has the capacity to eat large quantities at great speed and the ability to survive long periods between meals. In their search for a carcase, mammals mainly rely on their remarkable sense of smell, while birds depend more on their superb eyesight.

The part played by mammalian predators as scavengers has already been discussed in previous chapters, so it is only necessary here to summarise. Nearly all predators scavenge to some extent, but there is great variation; some, such as hyaenas and jackals, rely heavily on scavenging when circumstances allow, others do so opportunistically, particularly when live prey is scarce. With some species, size and numbers influence the degree of scavenging. Thus lions, acting as a group and being powerful, can easily see off hyaenas and cheetahs from a kill, while a pack of hyaenas may rob a leopard or cheetah of its prey through weight of numbers and persistence. As we saw in the last chapter avian predators such as tawny eagles also act as scavengers on occasions; however, it is the vultures that are the most specialised scavengers of all.

Vultures

One of the most remarkable, but not necessarily the most pleasant experience of a safari is to see a mass of vultures on a kill; a squabbling mass of birds hissing and squawking as they compete for food. But is it really as chaotic as it first appears? Careful observations will show that not all the vultures are alike. In particular, they differ in size, colour, markings and type of bill. There are six species you may see at a kill, but seldom all six on the one occasion. They can be classified into three groups according to size and behaviour, each with a couple of species.

The first group includes the two largest, the lappet-faced or nubian vulture and the white-headed. The former is a huge bird with a wing span of 2·7 m and a large skull with a massive bluish-grey bill, a purplish-red head and neck and naked folds of skin at the side of the head. The white-headed vulture is not quite so large, but has a conspicuous white head, neck and belly and a large red and blue bill. Both these species also occasionally act as predators, killing young antelopes, foxes, young birds and lizards.

The second group contains the two most common vultures, the white-backed and Rupell's griffon vulture. In the former the white back is only conspicuous when it moves its wings, while Rupell's has its wing coverts edged with white giving it a mottled appearance. Both have tough, hooked bills and long necks which are bare of feathers, a feature which facilitates cleaning after delving inside carcases.

The third group includes two smaller species, the hooded and Egyptian vultures. Both have small thin bills, the former, with uniformly brown feathers and the latter, mainly white with a yellow bill. Hooded vultures are also seen at refuse tips.

Each group plays a different role in dismembering a carcase. The hide of some herbivores is very tough and only the lappet-faced and white-headed vultures are able to tear away the skin. These species usually arrive first at the scene, either singly or in pairs. Once an entry has been made, the white-backed and Rupell's are able to use their long necks to advantage, delving inside to pull out the softer material. I have seen white-backed vultures standing on the back of a dead hippo which was floating in the water, putting their heads well below the water-line to reach the only point of entry and coming up for breath at frequent intervals. Hooded and Egyptian vultures pick up the smaller pieces dropped by the others and are often seen on the ground around the carcase. When most is consumed, the tough sinews can only be removed by those with the strongest bills, and the smallest left-overs, still attached to the bones, are neatly picked off by the fine, pointed bills of the hoodeds and Egyptians. By having these different roles, competition between species is reduced and there is seldom fighting between members of different species, but there are plenty of squabbles between those of the same, where the only rule is 'each for itself'.

If a herbivore is killed by lions, the vultures have to wait their turn. They may do so by wheeling on the thermals above the carcase, a sight which can alert hyaenas, jackals and those on safari to the location of the kill; but sometimes they may have to wait many hours, and their curiously humped shapes may be seen perched on nearby trees and on the ground around the kill.

Being heavy birds, it takes much energy to get them airborne, so, in the morning, they wait until the earth heats up and they can use the thermals to rise high in the air on their large, broad wings. They wheel over vast stretches of savannah from altitudes of up to 2000 m with hardly a wing beat; just specks in the sky to the observer below.

A remarkable feature of vulture behaviour is the speed at which a carcase is discovered and the little time it takes before large numbers have congregated. This is because they probably have the keenest eyesight of any diurnal animal. Their eyes are wonderfully adapted for seeing details from great heights by having the central portion modified to act as a telephoto lens with a magnification of two; and in addition, the retina has an extremely high concentration of light-sensitive cells in the region where the image is focused. This enables a vulture to follow the actions of predators below, notice unusual behaviour caused by an ailing animal and keep tabs on the activities of other vultures which are also keeping a look-out. If one bird spots a carcase, it swoops quickly down, others see the movement and do the same, and quickly many have gathered.

Vultures differ in their nesting habits. The lappet-faced and white-headed choose isolated trees, but white-backed nest nearer together, using a line of acacia trees near a watercourse, for example. They build huge stick nests lined with green leaves. Rupell's nest on cliff edges which gives them the advantage of easy take-off. Incubation takes seven weeks and the young are fed on regurgitated carrion. The young leave the nest when about four months old.

Marabou storks

These huge birds are often seen with vultures at a kill. Their bare heads and scruffy appearance as they stand by a carcase, explain their well-earned name of 'undertaker birds'. But see them in the air as they ride the thermals, or watch them as they return to roost, alighting on the pinnacle of a euphorbia tree with the precision of a helicopter, and they become transformed into birds of great beauty.

Marabous are much larger than vultures, but they cannot tear at flesh. Their role is to pick up scraps, using their long, wickedly-pointed bills. They are often seen around safari lodges where they make a living out of scraps from the rubbish dumps. Outside a fish factory near Kabatoro in Uganda, a hundred or more would stand in regimental formation in the sun for hours each day, waiting for the fish remains to be thrown out after filleting. Each bird would dispose of at least ten tilapia skeletons. Marabous will attempt to swallow almost anything; the most bizarre in my experience was a two foot piece of iron tubing. Fortunately for the bird, it could only partly swallow it, hard though it tried. They also hunt in the vicinity of fires for victims burnt to death, injured, or fleeing the flames.

Marabous make huge nests of sticks, and for the first few weeks after hatching, the chicks are fed largely on small vertebrates; not carrion.

Lesser scavengers

After the predators have had their fill and the larger scavengers have dealt with the left-overs, all that usually remains to tell the tale are the skull and a few of the larger, harder bones; even some of these tough remainders show tooth marks where hyaenas have gnawed at them. However, these hard remnants will not last for very long, as beetles will enter bone cavities and gradually destroy them and moths will lay their eggs on the horns. The larvae of these horn moths are able to tunnel into this tough material and gradually wear it away. So, before long, with sun, wind and rain, all will be returned to the earth once more.

Dung feeders

The dung of large herbivores contains much undigested material which is available for a host of species which depend upon it. Buffalo droppings, which resemble the cow pats of domestic cattle, may be very fluid when voided, and before the dung dries in the sun, insects are attracted to it, sometimes in a matter of seconds. These include various flies which not only feed on the more fluid material, but also lay their eggs within it. Time is short before much of the nutriment is lost, so the life cycle is appropriately rapid. The eggs hatch into maggots, which although they have no jaws, are able to absorb fluids and can liquefy more solid material with enzymes before intake. Growth is fast and a new generation is produced within a few weeks.

Elephants have a very inefficient digestive system and their droppings are much more fibrous than those of buffaloes and contain much material for scavengers. Giant millipedes, as big as a finger, and many species of dung beetle are attracted to the droppings for both food and moisture.

The dung-rolling scarab beetles quickly attract attention if seen on open ground as they trundle their balls of dung. Scarabs come in various sizes, the largest being huge by insect standards. They are sometimes attracted to the lights of safari lodges, blundering into walls and furniture and falling with a bang on the floor. Their very thick cuticle acts like armour-plating and gives them some protection against predators. If you pick one up, its movements are so strong, you have great difficulty in holding it.

Adult scarabs feed on dung, but some of the dung balls you see being rolled along are destined for the next generation. When ready to lay, a female will alight on a pile of fresh droppings, mould some of the contents into a ball and then roll it along the ground – she walks backwards on her front two pairs of legs while using the hind pair to push and manoeuvre the ball along. On reaching a suitable place she digs a chamber in the ground which is large enough to sink the dung well below the surface. Scooping out a hole in the ball, she lays a single egg, covers it up, and scrapes back the loose earth to bury it. The largest scarabs make dung balls the size of tennis balls and will bury them up to 1 m below the surface, sometimes ten or more together in the same area. When fully formed, the larva has only just enough room to turn around inside the ball, which by then is hollow as much food has already been consumed. It then pupates. When the rains come, the hard outer crust of the dung ball softens and the adult beetle emerges.

Scavengers on dead plant material

In temperate climates, earthworms are major scavengers on dead plant remains, but in savannah the soil is usually too dry for their survival. Their place in the ecosystem is taken by termites.

Termites

Termite mounds are a feature of savannah country. Some, formed by members of the genus *Macrotermes*, are as much as 7 m high and weigh tens of tonnes. In the Luangwa valley in Zambia, ancient mounds, often covered in trees and bushes, look like small hills with a diameter at the base of over 30 metres. They come in many shapes, differing in general style of architecture according to climatic conditions and the species that make them. Their colour varies according to the soil from which they are made. In volcanic areas such as Samburu, where successive layers of volcanic ash have been deposited, you may see red, brown, grey and white ones during the course of a single drive. Old mounds become more rounded with erosion and may appear quite polished after being used by elephants or hippos as rubbing posts. The whole structure, above and below ground, is composed of soil particles cemented together by saliva into an extremely hard and durable material.

Termites are social insects. A *Macrotermes* colony may contain several million individuals belonging to three distinct castes: reproductives, soldiers and workers. For most of the year there is a single queen and king, but prior to swarming, vast numbers of winged reproductives of both sexes develop and leave the colony to form new communities elsewhere. The queen grows to an enormous size for an insect – about 10 cm long and as thick as a finger. She can lay 30,000 eggs a day and live for 15 years. The king's only function is to fertilize the eggs.

The soldiers form about 2% of the population. They are wingless, sterile females with greatly enlarged heads armed with powerful jaws which they use to good effect when defending the colony against such intruders as safari ants. In some species, a particular category of soldier has the head tapered to a fine nozzle through which a noxious fluid can be squirted at the intruder. The fluid becomes sticky in air and may cling to the legs of the marauder, hampering its movements.

The workers, only a few millimetres long, are the most numerous inhabitants of the colony. Their pale colour has earned them the name of white ants, but this is misleading as they are not nearly re-

121

lated. They have no wings, are blind, and have very strong biting mouthparts. Workers are of both sexes, but sterile, and there are two kinds, major and minor. The former do most of the construction and maintenance work, while the latter carry out household duties such as collecting food, feeding members of other castes on regurgitated food, tending the queen and king and looking after the eggs and young.

Inside the mound just above ground level is the main nest. This contains the royal chamber in which the queen and king are permanently confined, an intricate system of chambers and tunnels which act as nurseries, fungus gardens and runways. The royal chamber has very strong walls and is suspended on pillars. Its only points of entry are a series of small holes through which only workers can pass. Workers feed the royals on regurgitated food, keep them clean and remove the eggs which appear every few seconds from the body of the queen. The eggs are taken to nurseries where they are stacked and tended. After hatching, the nymphs beg for food from any passing worker, who responds by exuding a drop of fluid from its mouth.

The fungus gardens occur in a series of chambers around the nurseries. They are made from chewed up wood pulp mixed with excreta and formed into convoluted structures which hang from the roof; fungi grow well on this pabulum. The workers feed largely on wood and cellulose, but they have no enzymes of their own to make these substances soluble; however, fungi have them, so by taking a nibble of fungus to mix with the pulp they have eaten, digestion can take place. In some termite species, protozoa occur in the gut of the workers to help in the same manner.

The microclimate of the mound is kept remarkably constant at a temperature of about 30°C and a humidity of 90%. Air conditioning is achieved by having a series of chimneys running through the mound which allow the hot air generated by the colony to pass out of the main exits and be replaced by cooler air from openings nearer the base. The smaller vents can be opened or closed by the workers according to weather conditions. The thick walls provide insulation, and the fungus gardens help to regulate the humidity. Under extreme conditions, workers use vertical tunnels they have dug to reach the water-table far below the surface. They bring the water back, drop by drop, and spread it on the nest surface where its evaporation causes cooling. The magnitude of the operation will be appreciated when you consider that a mound may evaporate 10 gallons of water a day.

Workers have a thin cuticle and may quickly become desiccated; they are also susceptible to strong sunlight, so they build tunnels below the surface of the ground which radiate from the mound in all directions, sometimes for 50 m or more. When a source of food is found, they cover it with a layer of mud which enables them to feed without being exposed. When you see the surfaces of old logs and dying trees coated with their tunnels, you know that a demolition job is in progress, carried out by these unseen workers, fragment by fragment. A colony can remove half a tonne of dead vegetation a year.

Once a year, at the start of the rains, vast numbers of reproductives develop in the colony ready for swarming. This spectacular event usually occurs after heavy rain and at night, although some species swarm by day. When conditions are propitious, workers make a number of slits near the base of the mound which are guarded by soldiers. Then the mound seems to erupt with emerging reproductives and its surface is soon covered with a seething, shimmering mass. Their flight is rather feeble, but with the help of wind currents they may manage to fly a few hundred metres. Great numbers are killed by predators: bats and nightjars catch them when in flight, rain frogs flick them up with their tongues as they wait by the mound's exit holes, and bat-eared foxes, aardwolfs, genets and many others may gulp them down with relish when they settle on the ground.

With a daylight swarming, swifts, bee-eaters, starlings, shrikes, hornbills, barbets and many others quickly gather for the feast. In the Serengeti, I once saw such an emergence when the sky seemed to be full of birds wheeling to catch them. They included 20 or more migrating kestrels which caught the termites in their talons and passed them up to their bills while still in flight. Even a pair of tawny eagles joined in the festivities, using the same technique for catching them.

In spite of such wholesale predation, some reproductives survive to form new colonies. When a female alights, she gives out a scent signal which attracts any male nearby; then she quickly hunts for a suitable site to make a nest, all the time being closely followed by the male. The wings, having served their purpose, are shed and the pair quickly forms a burrow. About a foot down, they hollow out a chamber in which mating takes place and a few eggs are laid. These hatch in about three weeks into nymphs which are fed on secretions from the parents. They are guarded until they become workers capable of taking over such duties as feeding and nest building. When the nest is established, a royal chamber is constructed in which the queen and king are confined for the rest of their lives, the queen gradually attaining her vast size.

In an established colony, the queen is killed by the workers when her egg-laying capacity declines, or if the king dies and she consequently lays unfertilized eggs. Certain nymphs, at an early stage of development, are then treated differently from the rest and become sexually mature. Several pairs of these reproductives may then take over egg-laying duties. Alternatively, winged reproductives may be forced to remain within the mound, the workers biting off their wings to prevent them leaving.

It is during the rains that some species spring-clean the fungus gardens. Workers bring the old material to the surface and spread it on moist ground near the mound. The fungi grow rapidly and form toadstools, and the termites use their spores to inoculate new material in the nest to form fresh fungus gardens.

One marvels at the intricacies of termite society and how adjustments are made according to community needs. When the colony is small, most young become workers; when it becomes short of soldiers, more are produced and when there are too many, some are killed. A key to how this happens is the mutual feeding that occurs throughout the colony. Reproductives and soldiers are fed by the workers, and workers exchange food from mouth to mouth. Thus the composition of the secretions which circulate reflect the contribution which each type of individual has made. So when the workers feed the queen, she receives a detailed chemical assessment of the state of the colony. The queen somehow processes this information and from her anal end she secretes drops of fluid which are taken in by the workers and spread in like manner from worker to worker. The fluid exuded by the queen has been likened to a computer print-out of instructions for dealing with the needs of the colony, such as having to produce more soldiers to compensate for losses after a raid. It is not known whether the eggs are influenced in some way before being laid or whether her instructions influence the actions of the workers, but the needs of the colony are certainly met.

Termites play a major role in the savannah ecosystem. They help to keep the soil in good condition for plant growth by making an intricate system of tunnels within the soil. These loosen the soil, cause rain to soak in more quickly, help plant roots to penetrate more deeply and allow more oxygen to reach them. In bushy savannah, many of the dense clumps of vegetation have their origins as isolated termite mounds. Due to worker activities and weathering, the mound and its immediate surroundings become richer and more favourable for germination of seeds, thus making it more liable to be colonised by termite-resisting plants of a shrubby nature. However, the ground just beyond this area becomes bare of vegetation due both to trampling by herbivores and termite activities and becomes a natural firebreak; so the bushes are able to survive and grow into dense clumps. The bushes in their turn provide protection for such trees as euphorbias during their early stages of growth, and when these grow large enough, they provide shade which favours other species. These interactions are typical of the effects of one species on others in a complex ecosystem.

Termites help in recycling plant material quickly. A dead tree, for example, under hot, dry conditions, takes much time to decay. But if eaten by termites, the nutrients take a much quicker route, as the termites in turn may be eaten by a host of other creatures and their products move rapidly through the food web.

We have already seen how myriads of reproductives are eaten during the swarming process, but throughout the year termites are also eaten as a welcome supplement by many species. Others, like the aardvark, have become completely dependent on termites; indeed the aardvark's structure and mode of life have become remarkably adapted to exploit this food source.

The aardvark has powerful limbs and immensely strong claws which are used for opening up a mound and its surrounding tunnels, and its huge ears are used for locating termite activity underground. The pointed snout has a fringe of hairs at the tip to filter out dust, and when feeding among the debris of a damaged mound, it first blows away the dusty earth before licking up the termites with its long, sticky tongue. In aardvark territory, you often see huge holes they have made in the side of mounds which they may use as shelters during the day. They are strictly nocturnal.

The pangolin is another termite specialist. At first sight, you would hardly guess that this scaly creature is a mammal. Its scales, which are modified portions of skin, are tough and sharp, and when attacked, it will curl up into a ball like a hedgehog, presenting the aggressor with a spiky problem few can cope with. It has a long, pointed snout and a thin, sticky tongue which can easily be extended into crevices. It has no teeth, so the termites are swallowed whole and crushed in the stomach. This is modified for grinding by having a hard lining and containing stones the pangolin has swallowed. Its massive tail gives the animal support when it digs with its powerful claws, and when attacked by the furious insects, can close its ear openings and nostrils to protect itself.

Many animals use termite mounds in one way or another. Cheetah, lion and leopard may use them as observation posts, elephant and buffalo may ease their itches by rubbing themselves against them and many smaller species use them as safe retreats. Old mounds are regularly used by banded mongooses as night shelters; they cram together in the hollowed-out central portion where the nest once was and also use mounds for breeding. Dwarf mongooses do the same, but being smaller, are also able to use occupied mounds by squeezing into the larger chimneys and shafts. Jackals may hide their young in a mound and genets occasionally breed in one. Monitor lizards use them as shelters during the heat of the day and may sometimes lay their eggs there. Spitting cobras also find their intricate passage ways to their liking and may take up residence.

When aardvarks have made huge cavities in a mound, they may be used by warthogs as night retreats, and hyaenas may lay up in them during the day. There is even a bird, the red-and-yellow barbet, which often nests inside a mound by making a tunnel in its side, and when the termites swarm, goes one step further and feeds its young on the reproductives so obligingly deposited on its doorstep. So, termites are not only essential scavengers of dead plant material, but their influence on the ecosystem is immense, both as a food source and a provider of fortresses which can be used by other species in so many ways.

We have seen in this chapter how dead animal and plant matter becomes the food of a great variety of scavengers; but the work of decomposition does not end there. It is then the turn of the fungi and bacteria which complete the recycling process by causing the decay of any organic matter remaining to produce the water, carbon dioxide and nutrients which the green plants use once more.

CHAPTER 11

Surviving Heat and Drought

In desert and semi-desert areas of north and north-east Kenya, very hot and dry conditions prevail for much of the year. The rainfall is scanty, coming only as infrequent, but often heavy storms. You enter this region when you leave the Kenya Highlands taking the Isiolo road which drops dramatically to the volcanic plains below. As you descend, the trees become shorter, and if there has been no recent storm, the thorny scrub becomes leafless, the grass turns from green to brown to pale straw colour, and the countryside becomes rapidly hotter and more dusty. If you go further north towards Marsabit or Lake Turkana you pass through many miles of this barren countryside. You see relatively few animals, as fewer species can survive under such extreme conditions and the majority are more active at night when the days are very hot. Samburu National Park gives you a taste of this country, but here the river transforms the vegetation and provides an oasis for a wealth of wildlife.

Tsavo and Meru National Parks are also hot and dry, but although these conditions persist for much of the year, rain falls seasonally and more predictably; however, annual rainfall is usually low.

In more typical savannah country, like the Serengeti and Mara, the climate is still hot and dry for most of the year, but the seasonal rainfall can be abundant and last for many weeks with heavy showers on most days. Showers may also occur spasmodically out of season.

In all these areas, plants and animals are subjected to long periods of hot and dry, and to survive they need to be specially adapted. The more extreme the conditions, the more sophisticated the adaptations have to be. If the rains fail or are inadequate, considerable losses may occur and only the fittest or more fortunate survive. The same applies when fires sweep across the plains adding another hazard for the fauna to cope with. Animals which cannot fly, flee or burrow before the flames reach them, perish in large numbers.

Following a drought when losses have been severe, populations do recover, but at different rates according to their reproductive strategies. The large herbivores have few young at a time, but as they bestow on them better parental care, more survive, but numbers increase rather slowly. Others such as small mammals and insects usually go in for large families, have many litters, or lay vast numbers of eggs; thus, if conditions become favourable again, numbers may increase rapidly.

Plant adaptations

Adaptations made by plants for surviving hot, dry conditions are mainly concerned with obtaining water and minimising its loss through evaporation. Some plants have very long roots which can reach the water-table far down below the surface, while others form large tuberous structures deep in the soil in which water, absorbed during the rains, is stored for future use.

The curious elephant-foot plant, commonly seen in Tsavo, has a water reservoir which looks like a small boulder on the surface of the ground from which tough, creeping shoots emerge. A different method is used by the baobab, the tree that the devil is said to have planted upside down because its crown of leafless branches during the dry season looks like a root system. This has no hard wood in the centre of the trunk like other trees, but a mass of softer, fibrous tissue in which much water is stored. Other plants have the ability of absorbing dew through their leaves; this can form in significant amounts in places where clear skies at night cause a big temperature drop.

Plants also have devices to prevent water loss. As most evaporation takes place through the leaves, by shedding these during the dry season, water is conserved. When the rains return, the latent buds quickly burst into leaf and within 24 hours the scrub begins to show green again. Others which retain their leaves, protect their surfaces with a thick, hard cuticle which is often covered with a layer of wax to make it even more waterproof.

Plants, in addition, protect their foliage against too much browsing. Some of the bright green shrubs you see throughout the dry season would quickly be eaten by herbivores if it was not for the fact that they contain poisons. Others rely on vicious thorns to make browsing more difficult when the leaves reappear.

As we have seen in a previous chapter, grasses may be grazed to ground level, any remaining leaves becoming brown and dead, but underground they have living rhizomes containing food and water, so that when rain comes they quickly sprout. These are all perennials, but annuals and ephemerals have a different strategy. They complete their growth and life cycle within the few weeks of the rainy season and leave an abundance of seeds which can withstand the hot and dry, as a legacy for the next generation.

Animal adaptations

An animal, faced with extremes of temperature and drought, has a number of problems to overcome. The first is to prevent the body from becoming so hot that vital functions are impaired. The ideal is to keep the temperature constant irrespective of climatic conditions, but few can attain this without losing too much water. The second difficulty is to keep the water content of the body as steady as possible, as severe dehydration may lead to death. The third is to find sufficient food when this is scarce and scattered. Finally there is the problem of reproduction and the survival of the progeny under such extreme conditions. The ways in which animals overcome these difficulties differ greatly.

Fish

At first sight, you would hardly expect fish to be mentioned in this context, but, nevertheless, they are present in waters which may dry up during times of drought, such as rivers which only flow seasonally, flood waters, shallow lakes and water holes – so they too have to cope in some way.

In the South Luangwa valley, for example, rivers overflow during the prolonged rains, dried-up rivers flow again, lagoons are filled and low-lying areas become marshes – and fish populate this flood water. During the long dry period that follows, the water gradually dries up. Some fish survive by making their way back to the permanent rivers, but others become trapped when the level drops. If the water is deep enough they may survive until the next rainy season, but if not, they become concentrated in great numbers in any remaining water.

I shall always remember coming upon such a situation when on a walking safari. It was soon after dawn, and what was once a lake had been reduced to a long narrow lagoon. It was an astonishing sight, because in the water and along its banks was a concentration of an estimated 700 yellow-billed storks all fishing madly. As if that were not enough, there was also a sprinkling of saddle-billed storks, ma-rabous, egrets and hammerkops, to say nothing of a pair of fish eagles which were already replete, perched in one of the surrounding trees. A few hundred metres away, another flock of some 300 yellow-bills were fishing out a further stretch of water. One began to feel sorry for the fish. Towards the end of the dry season these huge flocks fly from pool to pool as the waters recede and the fish become easier to catch.

In a tributary of the Mara river we once came across a seething mass of catfish that had collected in one of the deeper pools, the river having run dry elsewhere. Catfish are able to gulp air when there is a scarcity of oxygen in the water, so they can live much longer than most fish under these crowded conditions. They can also slither from one pool to another if the pool dries up completely.

Lungfish have an even more sophisticated answer to the problem when their habitat dries up. These large fish have an ancestry going back 300 million years and have evolved lungs in addition to gills. When the shallow waters in which they live are largely reduced to mud, they bury deep below the surface. They wriggle down tail first, blowing bubbles as they go to keep an air vent open through which they can subsequently breathe. Then they secrete mucus which har-dens into a waterproof envelope around them. Here they stay until the rains return and the hard cocoon of mud around them softens. They can remain in a state of suspended animation for two years or more if necessary.

There are also kilifish, no more than 50 mm long, which inhabit temporary pools and complete their life cycle within a few weeks. This period of frantic activity following the onset of the rains involves hatching from eggs, feeding up, growing to maturity, mating and fi-nally laying eggs in the mud before the pool dries up completely. The fish then die, leaving the eggs buried in the dried mud until the rains return and a new generation hatches out.

Amphibians

It seems like a miracle that in drought-ridden areas, as soon as the first heavy showers fall, the night seems to be filled with the piping and croaking of frogs and toads. During the long dry season these amphibians use various strategies to avoid desiccation. Some, like the burrowing toad and bullfrog, fill their stomachs with water and burrow into the gooey mud just before it hardens up. They secrete around themselves a mucilaginous covering which hardens and becomes almost impermeable to water, but oxygen can pass through slowly for respiration. The heart only beats spasmodically, and they go into a state of torpor or aestivation, just keeping alive with the help of fat stored in their bodies.

Some of the tree frogs use a different method, aestivating above ground and fully exposed to the elements. To prevent desiccation, they reduce their surface area by tucking in their legs close to the body and secrete mucilage which hardens to form a tough skin around them, rather like wrapping themselves in a tight-fitting polythene bag. In one species, the frog remains quite still for several months attached to the underside of one of the leaves of an evergreen shrub. Another tiny white species may occasionally be found in the grounds of safari lodges such as Keekorok, Amboseli and Kilaguni. They seem to like poinsettias, and remain quite exposed on the upper surfaces of the leaves. Only when the rains return will they become active again. Another species, the great grey tree frog, attaches itself to some exposed branch and aestivates for many weeks relying on its immobility to escape the eyes of predators. It loses as much as half its body weight through evaporation and food loss, but usually survives, nevertheless.

All these amphibians are only able to reproduce during the few weeks of the rains, so no time must be lost. As soon as the first heavy showers fall, they emerge from the mud or leave their positions on boughs or leaves and feed up rapidly. At night, the males make their courtship calls, coupling takes place, eggs are laid, and the tadpoles turn into frogs – with luck before the pools dry out again.

The great grey tree frog has a most elegant means of breeding. When the rains return, a pair will makes their way to a suitable water hole at night and climb an overhanging bough, the male clinging to the female's back. She then produces much mucus which is whipped up into a foamy mass by the rapid movements of the legs of both frogs. The eggs are laid into this foam nest along with sperm from the male and are thus fertilized and protected from desiccation. The eggs hatch quickly into tadpoles, and when the foam nest liquefies during further rain they drop into the water below and quickly complete their development into tiny frogs.

Reptiles

These have fewer problems than amphibians when faced with a long, hot and dry season as their bodies are protected by scales which reduce water loss and they are independent of water for breeding. Snakes tend to avoid the heat by being active mainly at night. They spend the day in burrows, either between roots or in termite mounds.

Some lizards use cracks between rocks to get away from the sun, particularly during the middle of the day, while others burrow into sandy soil to reach cooler conditions. Those which burrow, can do so extremely quickly with rapid movements of the feet, which by being unusually large, are very efficient digging organs; they disappear in a second or so. Monitor lizards may climb trees during the day to avoid the heat. I was reminded of this when a metre-long monitor fell out of a tree just in front of our vehicle. I'm not sure who was the more surprised. We were unable to find out what caused it to fall, but it soon recovered and quickly made its way into the undergrowth. If trees are unavailable, monitors may seek the moist, cooler conditions of a termite mound.

Tortoises may aestivate for long periods in clumps of evergreen bushes, withdrawing head and limbs beneath the shell. They can subsist for weeks on the fat built up during the rains.

Small mammals

Small mammals, particularly rodents, can survive quite well under hot, dry conditions. Being good burrowers, they can retire during the day to their underground homes where it is much cooler and the air moister; so the body loses less water to the atmosphere while breathing. They also have no sweat glands, concentrate their urine and pass dry faecal pellets. So water loss is minimal and many species can go without drinking altogether, relying on the small amounts of water present in dry seeds and vegetation to balance what is lost.

One species that does drink is the pygmy mouse, and it does so in a very ingenious way. It is a very small mouse, weighing little more than 5 g. It spends most of its time underground in an extensive burrow, coming out after dark to feed on small seeds and insects. It has the intriguing habit of collecting small pebbles which it arranges just outside the entrance to its burrow. During the dry season, the temperature often drops considerably during the night, so the cool air meets the warmer, moister air which emanates from the burrow. This causes drops of water to form on the cold pebbles which the mouse licks up towards the end of the night. Enough water is obtained in this way, and from what it gets from its food, to satisfy all its needs.

Birds

Birds can live for long periods in areas devoid of water as flight enables them to reach permanent water each day, if not too far away. However, few birds are able, or choose to breed, during the long, hot dry season, apart from the various species of sandgrouse. For this they are wonderfully adapted.

It is a splendid sight to watch at dawn or dusk by some water hole during the dry season and see wave after wave of sandgrouse coming in to drink. They swoop out of the sky, settle, bathe and drink; then off they go again with a whirring of fast wing beats. During the nesting period, they don't remain longer than necessary as they may have a flight of up to 40 km to reach water, and when there are eggs, these have to be temporarily abandoned at dawn and dusk so that both parents can drink. During the parents' absence the eggs are vulnerable to predation and over-heating, so no time must be lost. Water brought back in the male's plumage helps to dampen the eggs and the surrounding ground. This helps the successful development of the embryos.

When the chicks hatch, only the male leaves the nest to fetch water. On reaching the water hole he fluffs up his belly feathers and half submerges, drinking at the same time. He has specially adapted belly feathers with hair-like barbs which curl like springs and come together like a zip-fastener to form a tube which holds the water. Back at the nest, the young excitedly bury their heads among his feathers and squeeze out the water. They do this by running their beaks down the feather as we would use finger and thumb to extract the last remnants of tooth paste from a tube. All the water needed for both hen bird and chicks is brought back in this way.

One is tempted to ask, why go to all this trouble and breed in such an inhospitable area when it would be perfectly possible to nest much nearer to water? But there are benefits. If the difficulties can be overcome, there are different food resources which can be exploited and competition is far less; there will also be fewer predators to destroy eggs or young.

Large mammals

One of the greatest difficulties for a large mammal is maintaining water balance. In the longer term, water intake must equal water loss. Thus water taken in when feeding and drinking must equal that lost through sweating, panting, breathing and excreting. So the main adaptations are concerned with the manner of obtaining water and the reduction of water lost through these essential processes.

Large mammals have a great advantage over small ones by being highly mobile; like the sandgrouse, they can go long distances to find permanent water. Gerenuk and dikdik never drink, and some such as oryx and Grant's gazelle can do without drinking water, although they will drink if water is available. But even with these species, mobility is essential as the vegetation from which water is extracted may be widely dispersed and much searching has to be done. We have seen previously that some animals such as gnu, zebra and Thompson's gazelles take their powers of mobility a step further by making large seasonal movements to areas where permanent water is available.

Oryx organise their daily routine to get maximum benefit from the vegetation they eat. When very short of water they seek out plants called *Disperma* and feed on them towards the end of the night. This plant is dry and brittle by day and contains only 1% water, but at night, any dew that forms is absorbed through the surface and by 3 a.m. may contain as much as 30%. They will also dig up water-storage roots with rapid movements of the forelegs and quench their thirst that way. It is not known how they can detect the roots deep below the surface.

The Gerenuk gets all the water it needs by feeding on a wide range of plants and selecting the juiciest leaves. Its long neck, and its ability to reach high by standing on its hind legs, help it to make a better selection.

In order to reduce water loss to a minimum a number of strategies are used, but there has to be a compromise as essential processes such as breathing, elimination of waste and temperature control inevitably involve some loss of water.

Most species are able to concentrate their urine by re-absorbing as much water as possible as it passes down the kidney tubules. Water can also be extracted from the faeces prior to being voided; so the droppings of eland, oryx, gerenuk and dikdik are characteristically very dry. But maintaining body temperature without losing too much water is a major problem. Large mammals cannot burrow into cooler and more humid retreats during the heat of the day, so they have to rely on other adaptations.

One way of doing this is to reduce the effect of the sun's heat. A light colour reflects more heat than a darker one, so in hot arid regions the mammals have lighter coats than those of the same species living under easier conditions. This is very evident with Grant's gazelles around Samburu compared with those in Nairobi National Park. Oryx and the desert antelopes also have very light colouring.

The coats of these semi-desert species are hairy, but not woolly. Hairs are a help as they protect the skin from solar radiation and at the same time allow cooler air to reach the skin. This is important when cooling the body at night after a long day in the sun.

An obvious behavioural device is to be more active at night and find shade during the hottest part of the day, but shade is not always available; so just keeping still is better than nothing. By so doing, less muscular heat is generated which would otherwise add to the problem. Ruminants can make use of this inactive period by chewing the cud.

It has been suggested for the oryx, that its long pointed horns are such lethal weapons that they also help indirectly to conserve water and reduce temperature. Thus, if attacked by a lion, it might be better to stand and fight rather than run and overheat.

Many mammals control body temperature by sweating. Our own technique is to sweat as soon as our blood temperature exceeds the normal, but if we found ourselves wandering about in semi-desert scrub in the middle of the day we would lose as much as 1·5 litres of water an hour just trying to keep cool. At this rate it would not be long before we became seriously desiccated, and without water, would not survive more than a few days. But these semi-desert species manage to exist under these conditions without even drinking. How do they do it?

Clearly, sweating is not the best answer except only as a last resort. One method used by many species is to allow the body temperature to rise during the day, making little effort to reduce it until it reaches dangerous levels. If the animal can stand the temperature rise without damage to the tissues, the heat can be dissipated when the ambient temperature drops towards evening and particularly throughout the much cooler night. So the larger the surface relative to bulk, the quicker the animal can cool down. This increase in surface area is shown by the delicate shapes of these antelopes with their thin legs, long necks and large ears. Smaller mammals heat up much more quickly than large ones, so the latter have the advantage of having to cope with higher temperatures for shorter periods.

Oryx and Grant's can withstand temperatures as high as 46·5°C (normal is 38·1°C) for 6 hours without observable ill effects. Under these circumstances, most animals would get sunstroke, as the overheated blood would damage the delicate cells of the brain. But these species, and probably others too, have a special device for cooling the blood just before it enters the brain.

It was mentioned in Chapter 4 that the giraffe has a structure at the base of the brain where the carotid artery breaks up into a network of smaller arteries. This reduced the blood pressure when the giraffe stooped to drink. It is this same structure that helps cool the blood in oryx and Grant's gazelles. Here, thin-walled veins containing cool blood come into intimate contact with the network of arteries, and as the blood in the two sets of vessels flows in opposite directions, heat transfer is highly efficient, the temperature of the blood dropping dramatically before it reaches the brain. The cool blood which achieves this effect comes directly from the nasal sinuses through which air is being constantly passed when breathing. Here, evaporation of water from the extensive membranes lining these sinuses cools the blood circulating in the capillaries just below and is carried directly to the arterial network.

In many species, this technique for cooling the air in the snout, is used for reducing the temperature of the whole body, and is one reason why antelopes have long snouts. Although this characteristic is rightly associated with an acute sense of smell, it's function in temperature control is of the greatest importance. It may even be concerned in some species with water retention. In the camel, for example, the membranes lining the nasal chambers cover an area one hundred times greater than in humans and act as a one-way valve. So, when a camel breathes, it can absorb water from the atmosphere at night when the air is cooler and contains more moisture and also from the exhaled air from the lungs by day.

The dikdik, being so small, has the disadvantage of heating up quickly, but although it lives in semi-desert areas it is always associated with scrubby country where shade is available. When it heats up, its temperature is kept under control by panting. Under cool conditions its normal breathing rate is 30 breaths a minute, but at 40°C it pants at 400 breaths a minute. While panting, its proboscis-like snout acts as a bellows, so the hot dry air passes rapidly in and out over the nasal membranes with consequent evaporation of water and cooling. When it is very hot, dikdik move about as little as possible, doing most of the feeding in early morning and in the early part of the night. This explains why, during the heat of the day, they are so hard to detect under the bushes, and when seen will often allow you to take photographs from quite near without moving away. Panting inevitably involves loss of water, but dikdik are so efficient in conserving water in other ways that this method of cooling is very successful. Panting is also commonly used by other antelopes as a supplementary means of cooling.

It will be evident from the examples given in this chapter that the ability to cope with such extreme conditions and to occupy a particular niche in the ecosystem, depends on the combination of structural, physiological and behavioural adaptations of each species. It is this trio of inter-related adaptations that enable an animal to exist successfully whatever the ecosystem.

CHAPTER 12
Lakes and Rivers

The lakes that delineate so clearly the two arms of the Great Rift add greatly to the magnificence of the East African scene. Those in the Eastern Rift are shallower and their depths fluctuate considerably with changes in climatic conditions. Lake Turkana in the north is the largest (265 x 25 km), but even here in recent years the level has dropped dramatically, while L. Elmentaita, which is the smallest, has several times been on the verge of drying up during drought years. Lakes in the Western Rift, being much deeper, have suffered far less change.

Lake ecology varies greatly according to the degree of salinity of the water. Some such as Naivasha and Baringo are described as freshwater lakes as their salinity is not high enough to cause osmotic problems for their fauna, and land animals can drink from them without harm. A wide range of plants and animals can populate these lakes. Others, including Magadi and Natron have such a high concentration of alkaline salts (hence the term soda lake) that those who are foolish enough to wade in their waters for long are liable to suffer severe blistering of the skin. Here the water is devoid of life except for a few highly specialised forms. Between these two extremes there are lakes of varying degrees of alkalinity, some of which have thriving populations, but the diversity of species in them is usually far less than for freshwater. The higher the concentration of salts, the fewer the species that are able to cope.

When salt concentration is high, the main difficulty is that water is drawn out of the body osmotically. This causes desiccation even though the organism is surrounded by water. This loss of water happens because the concentration of salts in the body fluids is less than that of the water outside, and when the two fluids associate with a living membrane in between such as the gill of a fish or the skin of a frog, water passes from the weaker to the stronger. Some organisms have become adapted to these extreme conditions by becoming more tolerant to higher concentrations of salts within their own bodies, thus losing less water to the environment.

Freshwater lakes owe their existence to feeder streams, often from mountainous regions where rainfall is high. The purity of the water depends on the rock strata through which these streams pass. If the rocks are granitic or sandstone, few salts are dissolved, but with more recently formed volcanic rocks more salts will be taken up and pass into the lake. However, freshwater lakes also have exits so that any salts that do enter have little chance of becoming concentrated.

Soda lakes by contrast are like sinks without outlets. The water that enters them passes through volcanic strata where alkaline salts are dissolved, and because there is no outlet the salts build up. With constant evaporation from the lake surface and in some cases volcanic emissions from the lake bed in addition, the salinity increases still further. Only rain counteracts this build-up. In Lakes Manyara and Nakuru for example, the water level fluctuates considerably from year to year and season to season. During a long dry spell the water evaporates to such an extent that crystalline deposits form a white crust on the surrounding mud as the water recedes, but after heavy rain the level rises again and the salts are dissolved once more. With unusually heavy rains the surrounding trees may be inundated by the rising waters, and being unable to cope with the saline conditions, may die. The stumps of such trees may be seen around L. Nakuru, now taken over by cormorants which use them as nesting and roosting places.

Inter-relationships within a lake ecosystem follow the same pattern as those on savannah, with green plants as the producers of food and a whole array of animals dependent on them.

Producers

In a soda lake such as Nakuru you see no floating vegetation and the margins are bare, and to find the plants, you need to hold a sample of the water up to the light. It looks like pea soup and feels slimy. You do not see the individual plants as they are microscopic algae, but the millions present colour the water. This phytoplankton, is what all the fauna depends on. There are many species of algae, but those in soda lakes such as Nakuru mainly belong to the group of blue-green algae, and appear under the microscope as coiled chains, hence their scientific name, *Spirulina*. They are so abundant in places where fish cannot reach them, that they form conspicuous slimy masses on the lake bed.

In a freshwater lake such as Naivasha the phytoplankton is composed of plants of a different group, the green algae. These comprise a great diversity of species, many of which are motile, either as individual cells or colonies. Here too the concentration is staggering.

The success of these algae in both saline and freshwater lakes is due to the ideal conditions under which they live; the lakes are shallow, the sunlight strong, the temperature of the water around the optimum for photosynthesis and there is an abundance of carbon dioxide dissolved in the water. Consequently, much food is synthesised, growth is fast and reproduction can occur in some species every few hours simply by splitting in two. Lack of light is potentially a problem for them as the water is so green that light is unable to penetrate more than about 25 cm, but shallow lakes are so subject to wind and wave action that the water is thoroughly stirred up; this allows those species at lower levels to get a share of the light.

The waters are also very rich in nutrients. These may be in the form of salts dissolved in the water that enters the lake or are produced by bacterial action when dead products decay. The droppings of thousands of water birds such as flamingoes and pelicans and the dung of hippos provide much material for the bacteria to act upon. In parts of some lakes where hippos are abundant, as in L. Edward in Uganda, the bed of the lake is covered with an amorphous layer of their dung as much as half a metre thick. It so happened that this water was used to supply the bungalows at the Uganda Research Institute at Mweya, and there were occasions when taking a bath that the sweet smell of hippo added an exotic fragrance to proceedings.

In addition to the algae in freshwater lakes there is often floating or emergent vegetation which provides food for the fauna. Water lilies are often present, and at one time the shallower parts of L. Naivasha were covered in them to form a carpet of blue. However, some imported coypu found them much to their liking and destroyed them completely. Water lilies are well adapted for living in lakes. The main part of the plant is firmly rooted in the mud, but the leaves lie flat on the surface of the water and provide a large area for photosynthesis. Furthermore, when the water level rises, the leaf stalks grow very quickly and the leaf is not dragged under. *Salvinia* and Nile cabbage are other plants which clothe the surface of lakes, sometimes to such an extent that they become major pests, impeding boats and cutting off light from the algae below. Neither of these species are native to Africa and few animals will eat them, although I have seen hippos in Zambia chomping Nile cabbage when very hungry at the end of the dry season.

The herbivores

Microscopic herbivores occur in myriads in the plankton and feed directly on the algae which swarm around them. The commonest groups present are non-cellular protozoa, rotifers (wheel animalcules) and tiny crustaceans. The protozoa simply absorb the algae through their surface, but the rotifers suck them in with the help of rings of hairs which beat in sequence; these look like two revolving wheels when seen under the microscope. The crustaceans waft them into their mouths whilst swimming, filtering them off with a fringe of bristles before swallowing. It has been calculated that in L. Nakuru, which only has an area of 40 km^2, the plankton may contain 200,000 tonnes of algae and 2,000 tonnes of microscopic herbivores.

Larger animals can also exploit the plankton if they have a means of sieving it off. The most spectacular of these specialist feeders is the lesser flamingo.

Lesser flamingo

It is always a thrill for the visitor to L. Nakuru to see in the distance the broad band of pink around the edge of the lake which signifies the presence of perhaps several hundred thousand of these magnificent birds – if feeding conditions are ideal there may even be one million. They may also be seen in large concentrations on L. Bogoria and on the lake in Ngorongoro Crater, and in rather smaller numbers in many others. They fly from lake to lake according to conditions and only remain long in one area if the feeding is adequate.

They spend roughly 12 hours out of the 24 feeding, which they usually do when walking. They prefer to feed in calm, shallow water, walking with slow strides, head sweeping rhythmically from side to side. The head is held upside down and the blue-green algae are sieved off from the top 3 cm of the water. In order to keep the beak at this level, the lower mandible, which is on top when feeding, acts as an automatic float. At rest, the upper mandible fits tightly into the lower one, but when feeding, a small gap is left between them. The tongue lies in a narrow groove in the lower mandible and acts like a rapidly moving piston sucking water in and driving it out. When the water enters it passes over a fringe of hairs which lie flat, but when forced out, the pressure causes the hairs to become erect, so the algae are retained inside the mouth. When enough have collected, the mucilaginous mass is rolled on to the tongue where backwardly-projecting processes help to propel it towards the throat with the tongue's movement. Around the edge of the mandibles are stiff excluder hairs which prevent larger, unwanted particles from entering. A flock of 900,000 birds can extract 540 tonnes of algae a day (60 tonnes, dry weight) and put back 270 tonnes in droppings.

Lesser flamingoes are erratic nesters and choose very inaccessible sites; mud flats far from the shore have been used on such soda lakes as Magadi and Natron. Over a million pairs have been known to nest communally. Although they do not nest successfully at L. Nakuru, this is an important courtship display area. Display may occur over many weeks so the visitor may be fortunate to see this spectacle when thousands of birds mass together in a tight moving throng – a mass of pink on a forest of spindly legs – with neighbours fencing with their bills, carried high on necks held vertically. A few nests may be built here and eggs are occasionally laid, but reproduction is not successful.

On a breeding lake such as Natron, the birds construct huge numbers of nests. They are made from mud excavated by the beak, and appear as truncated cones 20–40 cm high with a slight hollow at the top. A single egg is laid and both birds incubate for the four weeks before hatching. By the time the chicks are eight days old they join up to form huge flocks which are guarded by only a few adults. In some places the downy chicks make journeys of many kilometres across the immensely hot mud flats to reach lagoons of permanent water where conditions are less extreme. Hundreds of thousands of chicks may use these traditional gathering grounds. Choosing such a hostile environment for nesting with the temperature of the mud by day reaching 55–65°C seems a strange thing to do, but it has the one great advantage that they are safe from mammalian predators, so the device appears to be worthwhile.

Greater flamingo

This species is often seen feeding among the more numerous lesser flamingo. They feed partly on blue-green algae, but most of their food consists of small invertebrates such as crustaceans and midge larvae, so they are not true herbivores. Holding their heads upside down they rapidly open and close their bills, sucking in and forcing out the water and mud which contains the food. This is caught in the fringing hairs when the water is expelled.

Herbivorous fish

There are also some species of fish which feed on the blue-green algae of soda lakes. Even in L. Magadi there is a small species, *Tilapia grahami*, which inhabits pools fed by hot alkaline springs. This 7–8 cm fish can withstand 40% salinity and a temperature of 39°C. It is thought that when it swallows this highly alkaline water along with the blue-green algae, it partly neutralises it with extra hydrochloric acid from its stomach. This species was introduced into L. Nakuru and has since thrived so greatly that it has become the main food resource for a host of fish-eating birds. It has been estimated that 250 tonnes of *Tilapia grahami* are removed from the lake every day by birds alone.

This fish has some engaging habits. Breeding throughout the year, the males choose a suitable area of the lake floor to stake out their half-metre diameter territories. A small pit excavated in the centre may act as a visual sign to passing females, as these territories are primarily used for mating. During the first few hours of each day the males defend these areas against any rivals by mouth to mouth confrontation, aggressively displaying their white lips. Little feeding is done by the males when on territorial duties, so when hunger calls, they all shoal off to better feeding grounds, all rivalry forgotten until the next morning when they are on duty once more. When shoals of females swim near, some which are ready to spawn are attracted by the antics of the males, and they enter a territory and mate. When the eggs leave the female's body she quickly sucks them into her mouth for protection, the male ejecting sperm into the water at the same time. The eggs remain protected in the female's mouth until they hatch, and later, the young fry are sucked back to safety if danger threatens.

In freshwater lakes other species of Tilapia graze on the prolific green algae. In lakes Baringo and George they are sufficiently large and numerous to support a thriving industry. For example, from

L. George, which only covers 20 km^2, 3,000 tonnes of fish are taken commercially every year. One reason for this is the great number of hippos present which enrich the water with their droppings. But there is a nice twist to the story as the fishermen are very wary of getting their canoes overturned and tend to avoid the shallower areas which hippos prefer; it is just these regions where the Tilapia breed, so the hippos unwittingly help to conserve the fish stocks.

Although flamingoes, Tilapia and other fish form the main bulk of the herbivores present in a lake ecosystem, there are, of course, many other species which feed on plants. Coot and duck may be present, including migrants from Europe. Some duck are true vegetarians, others include insects, molluscs and other animals in their diet. By feeding in different ways they exploit different resources; some are surface feeders, others up-end to reach submerged vegetation, while others dibble for their food. There are also plant-feeding invertebrates such as mussels, which lie almost buried in the mud of the lake floor and filter off algae and detritus, water snails which rasp their way through aquatic vegetation and the tadpoles of amphibians which in their younger stages also feed on plant material.

The carnivores

One of the fascinating aspects of lake ecology is how competition is greatly reduced between a large number of species which feed on a single resource such as fish. They do so by occupying different niches. This means that by using different hunting techniques, feeding on different prey, choosing different sizes of fish, exploiting different habitats within the lake or feeding at different times, each species is able to earn its living without treading too much on the toes of others. We will illustrate this by referring in some detail to the fish-eating birds.

Pelicans

Great white pelicans have pride of place among fish-eating birds as they occur in large flocks and consume most of the fish. Lake Nakuru has an average population of 10,000 pelicans which remove around 12,000 kg of fish a day, or 4380 tonnes of fish a year. On one occasion I saw a flock of about 3,000 mass-fishing on this lake. They flew in and landed in the shallows in a mighty throng. They all swam steadily parallel to the shore and immediately started to feed, holding their beaks just below the surface. The pouches acted like dip nets as they scooped up fish that were free swimming; other fish, no doubt, found refuge in the mud. As this vast flock moved forwards those at the rear found few fish, so took flight, leap-frogging the others to alight at the head of the flock. This manoeuvre was repeated time and time again.

Usually these birds fish in small parties of 8–12 birds, swimming in a horse-shoe formation with the open end forward. Three or four times every minute they simultaneously plunge their beaks into the water within the horse shoe. By working together they increase their chances of catching fish. They may fish like this for two hours or more at a time until those that are satisfied break away from the group. The pouch holds 13 litres of water, and not only acts as a catching device, but confines any fish caught while water is strained off before being swallowed. In freshwater lakes, white pelicans prefer to fish for larger specimens than the *Tilapia grahami* of L. Nakuru.

The pink-backed pelican, which is smaller and greyer, fishes singly and uses a very different technique. It searches for fish with head and neck laid back, then, approaching slowly, it suddenly shoots its head forwards and scoops up the fish in its pouch. When fishing in the same habitat as the great white, some competition is avoided by choosing rather smaller fish, although there is some overlap in size range.

Herons and egrets

A number of species may be seen, which are separated ecologically by their size, hunting techniques, choice of prey and habitat selection.

The goliath is a splendid bird, 1·5 m tall with a long, thick, pointed bill. Its larger size and rufous head and neck distinguish it from the more common grey heron. With its extremely long legs it can wade out into deeper water than other herons and can feed on larger fish. It stays motionless for long periods, but when it sights its prey, it lowers its body, partially retracts its neck and strikes with its mandibles slightly open, thus skewering the fish.

The grey heron prefers to fish in shallower water and feeds mainly in early morning and late afternoon. It too, stands and waits for its prey, but also walks slowly through the water, neck partially retracted ready to strike. It prefers smaller fish to the goliath.

The black heron is more local in distribution and has a remarkable fishing technique. It walks in the shallows, a few paces at a time, then flips its wings forwards to form a canopy over the water in front of its head. If no fish is to be seen it moves a few more paces and repeats the process. When fish are disturbed, they often seek shadow, so this may be a reason for the behaviour, but the canopy may also eliminate reflections, allowing the bird to take better aim. It may also make it more difficult for the fish to see the striking movements and take avoiding action.

The purple heron looks like a miniature goliath. It fishes in different parts of the lake to all the above, preferring reed beds, marshes and lake margins where vegetation is dense. It can also fish from floating vegetation, its long toes preventing it from sinking.

The great white egret prefers to fish on more exposed shores which are often wave-washed when winds are strong. It usually feeds while standing in water, waiting for any fish to come near enough for a strike. It catches its prey cross-wise in its bill and like all herons swallows it head first.

All these herons in varying degrees take other prey beside fish, including amphibians, crustaceans, aquatic insects and molluscs, but they are primarily fish-eaters.

Cormorants and darters

These use very different hunting techniques to herons, diving and pursuing their prey underwater with powerful thrusts of the legs. This enables them to fish in much deeper water than any other fish-eating bird. Their feathers are not completely waterproof, and the water absorbed makes them heavier – this helps them to remain underwater when pursuing prey. This characteristic also explains why you so often see them drying their wings after fishing.

On L. Naivasha, white-necked and long-tailed cormorants as well as the occasional darter may all be seen. At first, you would expect them to compete with each other for food, but work on their stomach contents carried out in Uganda suggests that their prey species differ considerably; of the 31 kinds of fish, 26 were found to be the exclusive food of one or other of the three species. The long neck of the darter, which gives it its other name of snake bird, is used in the manner of a heron's. When following a small fish underwater, it swims with neck partially retracted, and on nearing its prey makes a sudden forward neck thrust, spearing it with its bill.

Competition between these three species is also lessened by their preference for different habitats. White-necked cormorants thrive equally well in both soda and freshwater lakes and choose to fish in more open water; long-tails choose freshwater lakes and rivers where reeds and papyrus abound, while darters prefer sheltered, shallow, freshwater lakes fringed with trees.

Fish-eating raptors

The visitor cannot fail to be stirred by the clarion call of the fish eagle which is uttered with the head thrown far back. It is a wild haunting cry, which in favoured places, such as L. Naivasha, may be heard echoed quickly by others holding territories around the shore's edge. They are particularly vocal at first light.

The fish eagle, like the osprey with which it often associates, catches its prey in its talons. It usually watches the water from a perch in a lake-side tree until it sees the flash of silver as a fish turns. It then glides towards its prey, throws its feet well forward and strikes backwards, lifting the fish bodily out of the water with heavy wing beats. Fish weighing up to 1·5 kg can be caught in this way.

Although fish are their main food, they also take water birds, even killing adult flamingoes on occasions. They are also strongly piratical, attacking herons and pelicans and robbing them of their catch.

At night in some areas, the fishing owl uses the same technique as a fish eagle. Unlike other owls, its feet and legs are free of feathers, its claws are exceptionally long and the soles of its feet are rough to help grip slippery prey. They are large, reddish-brown birds capable of catching a 2 kg fish. They are not uncommon in the South Luangwa National Park in Zambia and may sometimes be seen flying in the late afternoon.

Terns and gulls

These exploit the smaller fish by circling over the water and diving. Terns feed mainly on fish although they also take aquatic insects, but gulls also do a lot of scavenging. When fishing, they prefer open water and choose the smaller fish, catching them in their bills.

Kingfishers

The most common fish-eating kingfishers (some species feed on insects) are the malachite, the pied and the giant. Again, these species compete very little with each other for food as they differ greatly in size, fish in different ways, choose different habitats and feed on different sizes of prey.

The tiny malachite kingfisher fishes from a perch overhanging shallow water and dives in to catch small fish. The pied kingfisher hunts further out, but prefers shallow water where it can see the fish more clearly; it hovers with head held downwards and then dives on its prey, catching it in its bill. The giant kingfisher is by far the largest of the African kingfishers and is capable of catching bigger fish than the others. It prefers lakes bordered by trees and will perch on an overhanging branch, watching the water below for any signs of fish.

There are also a number of water birds which primarily exploit other prey beside fish. These fill further niches in the lake ecosystem.

Storks

The three species that are often seen around lakes are the saddle-billed, yellow-billed and open-billed stork. The magnificent saddle-billed is 1·5 m tall. It may stand in water, striking at any fish that comes near, but more often it frequents more marshy areas where it probes between the vegetation with its very sensitive bill until some fish or frog is touched, when it strikes. It will also take reptiles and small mammals which live in these areas.

The yellow-billed stork may often be seen wading in water with its bill slightly open and immersed to near the base. It moves very slowly, stirring up the mud with one foot to dislodge any prey. The end of the bill is very sensitive to touch and if prey is contacted the bill instantly snaps shut. This species is very versatile, exploiting both soda and freshwater lakes

The open-billed stork has a curiously-shaped bill with the lower mandible curved in the middle to form a hollow. It specialises in snails and mussels. When a snail is caught it is held under water by the upper mandible while the lower one, which is like a knife blade, is inserted to cut the muscle which fastens the snail to its shell. It can then pull out the edible part in one piece. With mussels it forces its lower mandible between the two valves and cuts the muscles so that the valves open and the contents can be swallowed.

The hammerkop

This strange-looking brown bird with its large crest and strong pointed bill will hunt in any lake, marsh or stream where it is able to catch little fish, frogs, tadpoles and aquatic invertebrates. It prefers a situation where there are tall trees nearby where it can construct its huge nest. This hollow, domed structure, made of long sticks and vegetation cemented internally with mud, may be 1·5 m in diameter and weigh up to 50 kg! It is not surprising that such a desirable residence should be usurped by others on occasions. The eagle owl may take it over during its construction, and barn owls and grey kestrels may nest in it later. Egyptian geese often construct their own nest on top of the hammerkop's, and during the day an abandoned nest may be used as a refuge by a python, monitor lizard or genet.

A hammerkop feeds mainly in shallow water, using one foot to disturb the mud and snapping at anything disturbed by the action. When fish are passing up swift-running streams to spawn, a hammerkop will stand on the bank where the stream is narrow, gazing intently into the water ready to pounce if a fish swims by. A good place for seeing this is in Meru National Park where there are a number of narrow streams which are easily watched from one of the tracks.

Jacanas or lily-trotters

These are highly specialised for obtaining aquatic insects and molluscs by walking on floating vegetation. Their extremely long toes enable them to walk on lily pads, Nile cabbage and *Salvinia* with ease. When feeding they flip over a leaf with their bill and keep it in position with a foot as they search the underside for prey. They are usually seen wherever sufficient floating vegetation occurs; they are particularly common on L. Baringo, for example. The black crake and long-toed plover have rather similar habits and may often be seen along with jacanas. Another species which eats rather similar prey is the little grebe, but this common bird swims on the surface of the water and dives to find its food.

Spoonbills and ibises

Spoonbills are commonly seen in company with storks. They prefer to wade in shallow water, sweeping their bills from side to side and snapping at small prey such as small fish, crustaceans and aquatic insects. The strange spoon-like end to the bill makes catching more efficient as it adds to the surface area of the tip. Hadada, glossy and sacred ibis are seen more often in marshy areas and at the lake edge where they probe for small invertebrates with their long down-turned bills.

Birds of the lake margins

When examining the lake shoreline, particularily if mud is exposed, it is very usual to see a number of small birds, many of them waders, busily probing the mud for small invertebrates, or picking off flies from the surface. Their numbers are greater between October and February as many are migrants from Europe. Commonly seen are the diminutive little stint, sandpipers of different species, ruff, greenshank, long-legged stilts, black and white avocets with up-turned bills, and snipe and godwits with long straight ones. Plovers, which have shorter bills than waders, also frequent these feeding grounds, and range in size from the tiny 3-banded plover and Kitlitz sand plover to the handsome black and white blacksmith plover which makes a hammer-on-anvil alarm call.

This congregation of many species in one habitat is made possible by the rich and varied resources present along the shore-line and the great variety of techniques used in its exploitation. Identification can be left to the experts, but the visitor will gain much by just watching and marvelling at their adaptive behaviour. Varying lengths of leg allow different depths of water to be utilised; varied lengths of bill, the depth of mud that can be probed; and the different shapes of bill allow a variety of techniques to be used for finding and capturing prey. The long, strong bill of the godwit is used as a drill, the thin, pointed bill of a sandpiper is ideal for picking off individual items from the surface, and the up-turned bill of the avocet is just right for making sideways sweeps while walking in shallow water – but these are just a few examples.

Other carnivores

Birds are not the only carnivores which exploit the animal life of a lake system. In many lakes there are species of carnivorous fish such as lungfish, catfish, mudfish, Nile perch and tigerfish which take their toll of the smaller ones and a variety of other prey according to species.

Monitor lizards also enter the water to feed, even dropping on prey from an overhanging bough as it passes by. I once saw a large specimen bringing to land a catfish which was so big it had great difficulty in dragging it up the bank. It held it in its mouth and had to straddle it beneath its body to prevent its escape. The largest carnivore in the lake system is the crocodile, but this is not present in all lakes and often prefers the rivers. This species will be described fully in the next chapter.

Scavengers and decomposers

A lake ecosystem has many scavengers. Tiny crustaceans may be present in huge numbers, some of which feed on plant detritus and the remains of dead animals; in some lakes there are larger ones too – crayfish for example, were introduced into L. Naivasha and have thrived. Although they also take live prey, they scavenge dead fish and other similar material. I was surprised one morning soon after dawn to find numbers of these crayfish on the lawn of the L. Naivasha Hotel. They are active mainly at night, and these were the stragglers making their way back to the water. On wet nights they can keep their gills sufficiently wet to breathe on land without difficulty. When disturbed they raise their red claws menacingly – quite enough to make a small predator think twice before attacking.

An important scavenger in most lake systems is the blood worm. It lives in mud at the bottom and feeds on detritus. These minute thread-like creatures are not true worms, but are the larvae of lake flies. When they hatch, they are sometimes so numerous that they can appear like smoke coming from the lake surface (p. 112–113). They are consumed by a great variety of fish and water birds.

Finally there are the teeming bacteria which bring about the decay of any organic matter remaining and make available the simple substances which the green plants need.

Thus a lake ecosystem is a complex community of inter-dependent organisms, a largely self-perpetuating system through which the energy derived from the sun and material made by the green plants passes from individual to individual, and from species to species in a cyclic manner. This system is not wholly self-contained as some energy and materials are constantly being lost to other ecosystems, such as when fish-eating birds void their droppings on land or die away from the water. The system also gains in a variety of ways, as when hippos, which feed on land, defaecate in the water. The system is also liable to considerable fluctuations. Climate greatly influences the level and quality of the water and the populations of plants and animals change much from season to season and year to year as a consequence. But it is human activities that can have the greatest effects of all. Pollution from sewage, fertilizers or factories can rapidly cause the collapse of the whole delicate system, and even where little pollution occurs, gross over-fishing can have a profound effect on relationships within the ecosystem.

CHAPTER 13

Being Amphibious: Frogs, Crocodiles and Hippos

As the name implies, an amphibious animal is one that lives a double life, spending much time both in water and on land. Frogs and toads, crocodiles and hippos are all amphibious and they occupy key niches in freshwater ecosystems.

Although so different in many respects, they all use lungs when adult. Crocodiles and hippos use no other method of respiration, so when in water, they have to come to the surface periodically to take in air, but frogs and toads have rather inefficient lungs and supplement their oxygen supply by using the well-vascularised membranes lining the mouth. Frogs also use the surface of their skin which is kept moist with mucilage to help diffusion.

Frogs and toads are amphibians by classification. As adults, their various methods of respiration allow them to live on land where they obtain their food, but they are still tied to the water for reproduction as their spawn is unprotected and would soon dry up and die if left exposed. As tadpoles they have no lungs at first and have to breathe through gills or their body surface, but over the period of metamorphosis, lungs develop and limbs replace the tail as an organ of locomotion.

Crocodiles are reptiles and have more efficient lungs than amphibians, so there is no longer the need to retain a thin skin as a supplementary means of respiration; this has enabled them to evolve a protective layer of hard scales. They are also independent of water for reproduction as their eggs are protected by a tough shell and there is now no need for an aquatic larval stage as the embryo is surrounded by its own tiny pool of water within the egg. But although the crocodile is equipped to breed on land, it feeds when in the water, finds protection there and uses water to help regulate its temperature.

Hippos, being mammals, are basically designed as terrestrial animals and feed and breed on land, but they use the water during the day as a safe refuge and a place where they can keep cool.

All these amphibious animals are well adapted for living in both habitats and have evolved remarkably similar anatomical features which allow them to breathe air and keep alert when resting in water with their bodies almost completely submerged. They do this by having their nostrils, ears and eyes just above the water-line. To take a leaf out of Kipling's book you could say that if a frog's nose was pulled and pulled until it was long and thin, it would then have the profile of a crocodile, and if you gave a crocodile's head more depth by pulling from below it would resemble a hippo's!

Sufficient has been said in Chapter 9 about the way of life of frogs and toads, but it needs to be emphasised how important they are in aquatic ecosystems as they are a staple food of many of the larger water birds. More needs to be said about crocodiles and hippos as these are of great interest.

Crocodile

These contemporaries of the dinosaurs have changed little over the past 170 million years. Like mammals and birds, they possess a four-chambered heart which enables them to have two separate circulations, one to the lungs and one to the rest of the body; this prevents the mixing of oxygenated with deoxygenated blood and so makes oxygen supply to the tissues more efficient.

Controlling body temperature

Crocodiles exhibit a high degree of temperature control, being able to keep body temperature within +/- 4°C during a 24 hour period. They do this by carefully selecting a habitat where some shade is available and by having a routine daily programme which makes the best use of the differing properties of water and land for absorption and retention of heat. Although the routine may be modified according to the weather on different days, crocodiles usually spend the night in the water which retains its heat longer than land, and haul out in the morning to warm up again in the sun. Then, before they get too warm, they either seek shade on land or go back to the water to cool off, coming on land once more during the second half of the afternoon to get thoroughly warm before returning to the water before dark. This routine means that the visitor will get the best crocodile watching in early morning and late afternoon.

At Samburu, when the river was reduced to a trickle, I have seen crocodiles which have been unable to submerge completely, allow what water there was to flow through their open mouths and cool them that way. In the heat of the day they will also lie with their mouths gaping to cool themselves through evaporation of water from the lining membranes.

Size and locomotion

You seldom see a crocodile over 5 m long these days as there has been so much poaching for their skins, but a few do still occur. I visited one isolated area of the western Serengeti where there were some very big ones. They were so shy, you had to approach the river bank by wriggling on your tummy; then when you lifted your head you just got a brief glimpse of the monsters as they dashed for the water. Their actual size was later estimated by scientists who placed measured bamboo poles on the sand where they regularly basked and then photographed both poles and crocodiles from the air for comparison.

Being so heavy and having short limbs, they are not built for speed on land, but when disturbed they can cover the distance to the water very fast, sliding on their bellies and paddling with their limbs. When walking in a more leisurely manner they lift their bodies off the ground so that they appear curiously arched in the region of the hind limbs. In water they can swim well, quietly approaching prey with slight movements of the tail, or extremely rapidly by lashing, sideways movements of the same organ.

Feeding

Crocodiles regularly come on land at Samburu where food is put out for them and visitors are able to see these great beasts from close range. Other animals such as genets and ratels may also be attracted to the food and interactions between them and the crocodiles can be watched. They are safe from the crocodiles if they approach head-on as a crocodile cannot lunge forward quickly, but are in great danger if they are at the side as the crocodile can twist side-ways with incredible speed and catch one in its jaws.

Basking crocodiles may appear to be asleep, but they should always be treated with the greatest caution. If an antelope passes near, the crocodile will suddenly swing its tail round and knock it off its feet, often breaking its legs; people have been killed in this way too. Crocodiles are also a great danger to animals coming down to drink. In the Luangwa river and its tributaries there are many crocodiles, and antelopes approach their favourite drinking places with great caution. They stand near the edge for many minutes peering into the muddy waters for any signs of movement, ready to jump back if attacked; a submerged crocodile was seen to leap half out of the water in an attempt to grab a puku. It leaps by making a sudden, powerful movement with the tail.

On one occasion a tourist was watching a giraffe going down to water to drink, with camera poised for a picture. He got more than he bargained for, because when the giraffe's muzzle reached the water a crocodile grabbed it. The giraffe with an instant reflex jerked its neck upwards and the photographer got a picture of a 2 m crocodile hanging in mid air gripping the face of the giraffe. It is a moot point who got the greater surprise, the giraffe, the crocodile or the photographer. The threshing crocodile soon let go, but the giraffe lost its balance and fell into the water after it. However, it got to its feet, reached the bank and stood there, just shaking its head. Its face was badly lacerated, but it was able to walk away into some bushes and looked as if it would survive.

Crocodiles will attack large animals when they wade into water or attempt to ford rivers; many gnu die in this way during their migration. The weight of the crocodile combined with its violent body contortions cause the animal to fall; it is then pulled under and death is by drowning.

Crocodiles cannot chew their food as their jaws are tightly hinged, allowing only up-and-down movement. Their rows of sharply-pointed teeth are for gripping and tearing off whole chunks of flesh while they twist and turn. To make the dismembering of a large carcase easier it may be left in the water for days, but this is not always possible as other crocodiles may compete for the spoils. It is not a pretty sight to see a dead hippo being pulled to pieces by a group of crocodiles all thrashing about in the water, pulling, twisting and rolling as they rip off mouthfuls.

One of the difficulties a crocodile has when trying to drown large prey is its own buoyancy when submerged. This may account for the strange habit of swallowing stones and keeping them permanently in the stomach. Young animals have no stones, but all adults do. They amount to about 1% of their weight on land, but in water this ballast is a very significant extra, adding as much as 15% to its submerged weight as the stones do not add to its volume. The stones lie against the under belly of the animal and so lower its centre of gravity, enabling it to lie on the bottom more easily. The additional weight may also give them extra stability when living in fast-running streams or below waterfalls.

Breeding behaviour

During the breeding season in places where crocodiles are numerous, the large males have territories which they patrol and defend from neighbours. If a female enters a territory, a prolonged courtship ritual may take place before mating. Approaching the female in the water, he may submerge and then lift his head above the surface with jaws open. He then raises his tail so that it forms a semi-circle with its base and tip in water. He then sinks and masses of bubbles come to the surface exhaled from his gullet. This 'bubble display' is often followed by what Hugh Cott describes as a 'splash display' when the jaws are lifted still higher and smacked hard on to the surface of the water. At the same time the tail is lashed from side to side and the jaws snap together. The male may also give a 'fountain display' forcing out air when his nostrils are just below the surface to form a spout of water droplets. In spite of these elaborate displays the female is often unimpressed, however, when she is ready to mate she will draw attention to herself by rearing her head and shoulders out of the water vertically and make a prolonged creaking vocalisation. Mating takes place in shallow water.

The female chooses the nest site with care. As she will guard the nest for three months, a site is preferred which has shade nearby where she can remain on guard during the heat of the day. A sandy bank near permanent water is ideal as this is easy to excavate and the temperature and humidity of the soil is usually near the optimum for successful incubation. On the banks of the Nile egg laying takes place during the dry season when the water is receding, and the eggs hatch before the rains, thus avoiding possible flooding. The nest is dug to a depth of around 45 cm, which in an exposed, sandy situation will maintain a temperature of about 30°C with only slight fluctuations. During incubation the female guards the nest by lying on top of it or nearby, as the eggs are vulnerable to predators such as marabous, baboons, ratels and monitor lizards. She feeds very little during this period.

When Hugh Cott was studying the breeding habits of crocodiles in Uganda, he took my wife and me to some of the nesting sites. One particular nest was due to hatch and as we approached, the mother slipped into the water and anxiously watched us from a distance. The young are sensitive to vibrations and respond by making croaking sounds. This is the signal to the mother that they are about to hatch. It was a great thrill to hear these sounds when we placed an ear to the ground. On scooping out the sand we found 30 eggs, some were just cracked and a few showed a beady-eyed head poking out from the leathery shell; one, fully out was 32 cm long. It is astonishing that an animal of that length can emerge from an egg the size of a goose's egg. The sand was shovelled back and we left the mother to attend the hatching. Usually, she excavates the soil herself as it becomes too compacted during incubation for the young to dig through.

When the young are free, both parents may help in carrying them to the nursery area which is often a shallow inlet with plenty of hiding places. They are gently carried by mouth, several at a time, and may be seen poking out from between the partly-opened jaws. Further down stream we were very fortunate to see a clutch of 25 2-day old young sunning themselves on a half-submerged log. It was interesting that the log showed a remarkable likeness to a crocodile's head because the young are known to rest on their mother's snout on occasions. When our boat glided to within a few metres of them, they slipped into the water and swam under some weed. The mother guards her brood for a few weeks, after which they disperse and live independent lives.

Crocodiles become mature when around 18 years old. This makes conserving them more difficult, because when crocodiles become infrequent a greater proportion of animals under this age are poached and less breeding takes place. In some areas crocodiles have been poached out completely, but the formation of a number of crocodile farms has helped the situation marginally. The skins are used mainly for shoes and handbags.

Hippopotamus

A bull hippo can weigh over two tonnes and run as fast as a man. When running, its short sturdy legs move very quickly, and from a distance the hippo looks like an animated sausage, but if it's coming towards you it looks much more like a tank and it's well to take avoiding action. Hippos should always be treated with great caution, particularly when you are on foot and if you are between the animal and the water.

The skin is well adapted for life in water. It has few hairs apart from some bristles on the muzzle, and a very thick lower layer, or dermis, covered by a very thin epidermis – so thin that water can be absorbed through it. However, this has the disadvantage that much water is lost through evaporation when on land, and is the main reason why hippos spend much of the day in water and feed at night. Hippos have no sweat or sebaceous glands, but they do have glands which secrete an oily substance which contains a red pigment. This dries on the surface and acts as a barrier to ultra-violet light and serves both as sunburn lotion and as a useful antiseptic. Hippos suffer severe wounds when fighting and often live in foul water, so this 'ointment' probably helps fast healing. The pink colour accounts for the myth that hippos sweat blood.

Although hippos spend most of the day in water, in very secluded places they may venture on land for short periods at any time, but they keep near the water and quickly return to it if disturbed. On one memorable occasion in the Busanga Plains area of Kafue National Park, Zambia, we made our way on foot to a river to see hippos. Although it was early afternoon we were surprised to find that the whole herd of 82 hippos were out of the water sheltering under trees about 50 m from the bank on the opposite side. The river was about 20 m wide. When they saw us, they immediately stampeded for the water in our direction, entering the river just opposite to where we were standing. As animal after animal charged headlong into the water the river was churned up into a cauldron of foam. We were relieved that we were on the right side of the river.

Hippos can swim quite well. At Mzima Springs, in Tsavo Park, there is an observation room below water level where you can view the underwater life. If you are fortunate you may see a hippo swimming by or walking on the bottom. Due to the buoyancy of the water, when you see one walking, you are reminded of the TV pictures of man's first steps on the moon; the hippo just bounds along, stirring up mud with each long, bouncing stride. Before submerging, ears and nostrils are closed by valves; it can remain below for up to six minutes.

Feeding

Hippos have been described as 'nature's best mowing machines'. Having such wide mouths, held close to the ground, they certainly mow the grass remarkably fast. In Uganda, the lawn of our bungalow needed little extra attention after the hippos had paid us a visit. Hippos feed mainly on grasses which they pluck with their lips, making a lot of noise when doing so. They need about 40 kg of food each night; not very much for a herbivore of that size, but sufficient, as they use up very little energy during the day while lazing in the water.

The grass in the vicinity of a lake where hippos are numerous is quickly removed, and when they emerge from the water in the late evening they have been known to go as far as 2.8 km in order to find enough food. If there should be a convenient wallow or water hole where they can spend the night, they may extend their foraging distance to up to 10 km.

Overcrowding soon leads to erosion. When helping with a game count from the air in Ruwenzori National Park we were caught in a thunderstorm, and as we circled we could see the red earth being swept off the land into the water, colouring it for some distance out. At one time in this park hippos became far too numerous and their traditional paths from the water soon became erosion gullies. The Parks authorities decided that some of the hippos would have to be culled. Six thousand animals (50% of the population) were shot over a period of five years and their meat sold to the local people – 2.8 million kilograms of it. The result was dramatic; the grass came back and the populations of waterbuck, elephant and buffalo increased steadily over the years that followed. But the lesson learned from this drastic experiment is that if culling does become necessary, it is better to do a little every year, rather than kill great numbers at a time.

In regions like the Luangwa valley in Zambia where there is a six month wet season followed by six months of dry, hippo behaviour varies considerably throughout the year. During the rains much land is flooded and smaller rivers and lagoons contain a great deal of water, so hippo movement is greater and social groups are more spaced out. Grasses and reeds grow quickly during the rains and provide much food for the hippos which, due to their large numbers, are the dominant grazers in the fauna. At the start of the dry season in May, the grasses are very high, but as they dry out and seed, they become progressively reduced both in height and food value. Towards the end of the dry season the herbaceous layer has largely gone, having either been eaten, or trampled to form a broken straw covering. With water greatly reduced, during the day the hippos become progressively more restricted to the larger rivers and the permanent lagoons, so in September and October the rivers have their highest populations. At this season the hippos can easily be counted as the water is often too low for complete submergence and I have seen more than 200 in a single stretch of the river. At this time of the year feeding becomes more and more difficult and they rely heavily on the trampled straw, but may have to travel long distances to find it. When really short, I have even seen hippos in a lagoon munching Nile cabbage. They chew their food with their back molars, and much of the digestion occurs in the long caecum where there are bacteria and protozoa to help break down the carbohydrates. Starvation is a common cause of death when population density is high.

Social life and reproduction

A social group typically consists of 5–15 individuals comprising females and juveniles with one or more males. There is a dominant male which has reproductive rights over the females. The group occupies a territory of up to 500 m of river or portion of lake. Groups often coalesce to form large aggregations and this may lead to aggressive action between bulls. They threaten each other by opening their mouths very wide to display the long canine teeth and the pink throat; usually this is enough to cause one bull to retreat. I saw an amusing variation of this threat when one bull lowered its head slightly so that its lower jaw was well under water; it then closed its mouth vigorously causing a wave of water to enter the other's mouth with great force.

They also demonstrate ownership of a territory by defaecating in the water, turning their backs on each other, and rapidly moving their short tails from side to side, scattering the dung in the manner of a muck-raker. When threats are of no avail severe fights may occur, lasting up to an hour or more. I once saw a bull chase another right out of the water and along the shore line; the one in front then turned and they faced each other, opened their mouths to their full extent, reared up on their hind legs and attempted to attack the other's jaws with their tusks. The larger bull then went for the other's flank slamming its open mouth against its opponent and at the same time ripping upwards with its long, sharp lower canines. It sped away dripping with blood. Although wounding often appears to be very severe, the very thick dermal layer usually prevents damage to the vital organs. Most old bulls show scars from previous battles.

Hippos usually leave the water around dusk. Each group has its special exit path which is liberally sprayed with dung to act as an odoriferous sign of possession. They leave in line astern, and if the leader stops, the others have to wait, sometimes for minutes on end. When they reach their feeding grounds they spread out and start to graze. These hippo trails are easy to identify as they appear double with a line of grass in between. They are formed in this way because a hippo's legs are set far apart and follow the line of the path very accurately.

Females become mature at around nine years old, males a little earlier, but the latter do not mate until around 20 years old when they attain dominant status. Mating takes place in the water, with the female sometimes completely submerged and having to raise her head at intervals to breathe. The usual reproductive pattern is for mating to occur in the dry season when most animals are concentrated in larger rivers and lakes, and birth takes place eight months later during the rains when vegetation is lush and the females are in good condition for suckling. As lactation lasts a full year, the calves also benefit from an abundant food supply as soon as they are weaned.

Birth usually occurs on land, but has been known to take place under water. The new-born calf weighs about 40 kg and during the first few weeks keeps very close to its mother. Suckling may occur on land or in the water. The young are vulnerable to attack from crocodiles, lions and hyaenas, and losses may exceed 50% during the first year despite the care the mother shows for her calf, guarding it closely when on land and keeping near it when in the water. Sometimes she will take her calf to deeper water where it may rest its head on its mother's back.

The females are in poorest condition towards the end of the dry season, and if this becomes unusually prolonged may bear a calf before the vegetation has recovered. I once saw a cow which had died under these circumstances, no doubt from a combination of starvation and giving birth. A calf becomes imprinted on its mother at birth and this one refused to leave her side. For three days the calf remained close to her dead body, pathetically swimming round and round and taking no notice of the other hippos nearby. It was later killed by hyaenas.

Hippos have various associations with other animals. When half submerged they make excellent observation platforms for herons, cattle egrets and hammerkops, and tortoises and terrapins will clamber out of the water to sun themselves on their backs. Oxpeckers frequently settle on them and remove parasites from ears, nostrils and folds of skin, and certain fish clean their bodies under water from algae and other debris.

Hippos are very important members of aquatic ecosystems as they graze on land and defaecate mainly in water. In this way they enrich the water and indirectly provide food for algae and the whole food web dependent on them.

CHAPTER 14

Forests

Forests are exciting to explore. 'Explore' is the right term as they are mysterious places – one never quite knows what will be encountered, and off the tracks there are no distant views to help with orientation; all around is vegetation in all its richness.

There are three main types of tropical forest, montane, groundwater and coastal, and the visitor to East Africa may come across examples of all of them. Montane forest is found clothing the lower slopes of the great mountains such as Kenya, Kilimanjaro, Meru, Ruwenzori and the Virungas. It is formed because of the extra rainfall in these regions due to the rising and cooling of moisture-laden air when it strikes the mountain side. Groundwater forest occurs where the soil is kept constantly moist due to water seeping down from higher areas or from springs, and in East Africa it often occurs near the base of an escarpment, as in L. Manyara National Park in Tanzania and the Maramagambo in Uganda. It may also be present in the form of narrow strips bordering river systems, caused by water seeping outwards from the river. This riverine forest is very conspicuous from the air, the ribbons of green contrasting strongly with the parched countryside. Coastal forests are found where monsoon winds, saturated with moisture from the sea, pass inland; the air then becomes heated, rises, cools, and sheds its moisture some kilometres inland. Examples may be found a little way back along the East African coast.

The vegetation

All these forests have much in common although montane forests show much variation with altitude, with conspicuous zonation of tree species. In the Aberdares, for example, there are tracks which enable you to ascend through tall forest on the lower slopes, then through transitional forest to an altitude of 2300–2600 m where much mist and cloud causes enough rain and prevailing moist conditions to allow a profusion of mosses and lichens. Here there are trees with twisted trunks and rough-barked boughs festooned with the greyish-green drapes of Spanish moss (which is really a lichen). Above that, on the wetter slopes, is bamboo forest – a strange world of giant grasses with woody, closely-packed vertical stems up to 7 cm in diameter, leading upwards to a dense canopy of narrow leaves which keeps out so much light that the ground can be bare of vegetation. Higher still is the giant heather zone and the alpine moorland beyond. This zonation with local variations is found in most montane forests.

The productivity of a tropical forest is very high – often twice that of savannah at its best. This is because tropical forest occurs near the equator and enjoys all the habitat factors which plants like best: an abundance of light and moisture and a warm temperature. Conditions within the forest are remarkably constant throughout the year as there are no obvious seasons; there are only small variations in the degree of wetness and slight changes in temperature between day and night, which become rather greater at higher altitudes. Thus growth is fast and continuous and the vegetation luxuriant.

I was glad of the experience to fly low over the Maramagambo. Beneath was a carpet of green formed by the interlocking canopies of myriads of trees. There were many kinds, distinguished by slight changes in shape, texture and shades of green, with the occasional giant emerging high above the rest. Here and there were bright splashes of colour where trees were flowering, the brilliant orange-reds of the flame trees being especially striking. There were also a few breaks in the forest where hollows had allowed water-holes to develop; here the grassy patches surrounding the water were marked by muddy animal trails radiating outwards.

Forests seen from within, are twilight places as only about 5% of the light reaches the ground; the air is still and humid, and apart from the occasional calls of birds and monkeys and the faint hum of insects in the canopy, all is remarkably quiet.

The soil is fertile, as it is continually being supplied with nutrients from the deep layer of rapidly-decaying leaf litter above it, but with so much rain there is a danger of the nutrients being leached out. However, the forest canopy protects the soil from the direct impact of a storm. Covering the soil is a deep compost-like layer which acts like a great sponge, retaining a reservoir of water which the tree roots are able to utilise.

Most of the trees have shallow root systems which exploit the fertility of the upper layers of soil, but this makes them more vulnerable to storms which batter their exposed tops. The soil's fertility is fragile, and if the trees are clear-felled the surface layers are exposed to torrential rain, the humus built up over many years is eroded away, the nutrients leached out, and what is left of the soil is so impoverished that little will grow on it.

The structure of a forest is determined by the need to obtain light for photosynthesis. In high forest the trunks of many of the trees, often buttressed for support, ascend with hardly a branch until they reach the canopy where they produce a close cluster of boughs and leaves. Different species reach different heights, so the canopy is formed of distinct strata of vegetation and acts as a gigantic factory for food production. Below the canopy there are straggly trees, many of which are destined to die from lack of light before they reach the sunlight. Only when a tree falls and a gap in the canopy is formed, do saplings have their chance to grow to maturity. In parts of the forest where the canopy is not so dense, shorter trees and shrubs may form an under-storey.

The leaves of many species have evolved very similar characteristics which fit them for forest conditions. A typical leaf is large in order to maximise the available light, but small enough not to shade the lower leaves too much; it also tapers to form a drip-tip which acts as a spout for rain run-off. It is dark green, signifying a lot of chlorophyll for photosynthesis, and has a waxy surface. The wax makes a leaf shiny and so reflects the light upwards to other leaves, causes rain to bounce off the surface, allows it to dry more quickly, and makes it more difficult for mosses and algae to get a foothold. In addition, the leaves in the canopy are able to receive optimum light by adjusting their position in relation to the sun's movement.

Not all species reach the light by just growing towards it; some make use of their neighbours for support. Lianas, for example, are really trees which have lost their powers of self-support. Although they have their roots in the soil they make use of any young tree to take them to the sunshine. As the tree grows, the liana twists and turns among its branches, scrambling from one support to another and becoming stronger and thicker as it grows. Eventually, it reaches the canopy where it puts out most of its leaves and flowers.

The strangling fig uses a different method. A seed enclosed in a bird dropping may lodge in some humus caught in the crotch of a tree. After germination, it sends out aerial roots which grow downwards until they reach the soil; now, firmly rooted, it receives more nutrients and the plant is able to develop branches, leaves and many more aerial roots. After a few years of growth, its leaves smother the host tree which, being deprived of sufficient light, will eventually die. But by this time the fig roots have grown large and strong and are able to support the rest of the tree; so when the host tree rots the fig usurps its place in the forest.

Epiphytes are also very numerous. These are plants which make use of others to obtain a foothold, but do not extract nourishment from them as parasites do. Like the strangling fig, they start life in some humus collected in the crotch of a tree or in furrows in the bark. Many ferns and orchids are epiphytic. As the water supply is intermittent, many epiphytes have thick fleshy leaves or stems for water retention. Some put out aerial roots which are covered with a layer of tissue which is impermeable to water, thus preventing water loss; but where the root touches the tree, this layer is absent, and rain can be absorbed when it runs down the trunk. The majority of epiphytes are perched high up in the canopy and achieve this position because their spores or seeds are often as small as dust particles, and by producing vast numbers, there is a good chance that some will be wafted upwards on air currents and lodge in some conveniently placed humus.

The forest also has its parasites. Species of mistletoe are quite common on some of the older trees; they look like untidy, globular clusters of greenery hanging from a bough. Although they possess a few green leaves and can photosynthesise, they are dependent on their host for most of their food. There are also some strange root parasites. One of these, called *Thonningia*, extrudes through the leaf litter to form a conspicuous, large, orange-red flower with concentric rings of stiff petals. It has no leaves, and taps food from tree roots.

The trees mainly flower in the canopy. Here there is a host of pollinators ranging from beetles and butterflies to birds and bats. The relationships between flowers and pollinators are often wonderfully intricate; in some instances the plant is totally dependent on one species of pollinator.

Animals also help with fruit dispersal. The succulent ones are eagerly sought after by birds and mammals, and if they contain small seeds, these pass out with the droppings. Large seeds, which are typical of many forest trees, if too hard to eat, are discarded and fall to the ground; they contain much food reserve which enables a sapling to grow quite tall before it needs to photosynthesise very much, giving it a better chance of reaching the light if a gap in the canopy occurs.

Some ant species are great seed dispersers; most of the seeds are brought back to the nest as food, but many are dropped on the way and may germinate some distance from the parent plant, thus reducing competition between parent and offspring.

The cycle of events in a tropical forest is similar in principle to that of all other ecosystems, with producers, consumers and decomposers all playing their part as energy and materials pass from species to species within the food web. But compared with savannah, a higher proportion of plant material is difficult for the herbivores to utilise as more of the products of photosynthesis go into the manufacture of wood and cellulose to support the great trunks and boughs. This material, along with other nutrients, is locked up, perhaps for hundreds of years, before the tree dies and the decomposers get to work. The parts of a tree which are recycled more quickly are the leaves, flowers and fruits; these may become the food of animals and pass through the food web in the usual way or decay fast.

The fruits of many species are abundant, and as different kinds ripen at varying times, there is a continuous supply somewhere in the forest for those which are sufficiently mobile to reach it. This fruit harvest has provided a niche for several species of bird and mammal which are almost entirely dependent on this one type of food.

Leaves provide more of a problem to the herbivores, as when they get older, they rapidly form substances which make them indigestible or poisonous. Many leaf-eaters have evolved methods of overcoming this difficulty, but nevertheless, the majority of leaves remain untouched by animals. It is only when they are shed that recycling can take place with the help of scavengers and decomposers.

The consumers

The animal life of a forest is not easily seen as many species are small and most are confined to the tops, some spending their whole lives there. When walking through the forest, it is often difficult to spot animals in the dense canopy, even those as big as birds and mammals, so it is not surprising that those that live there have a similar problem; consequently, they rely on loud clear calls rather than sight to keep in contact with each other. I vividly remember an instance of this when sitting at the base of a large, buttressed mahogany tree in the Budongo forest in Uganda, watching a group of chimpanzees feeding on figs. Suddenly, as if at a signal, they all became alert, and a tremendous din broke out, the forest ringing with their weird hollow cries. The noise stopped as abruptly as it had started and in the distance the response from another group could just be heard.

A good time to hear the noises of the forest is at dawn. Then you are likely to hear the crescendo of raucous cries made by hornbills, the bell-like calls of shrikes, the three-part song of the red-chested cuckoo, the drumming of woodpeckers, and a chorus of bird song from the canopy. At night a forest is even more noisy with the stridulations of many crickets and cicadas, the piping of tree frogs and the hooting of wood owls.

The food webs and interrelationships in a forest ecosystem are far too complex to describe in detail, so only a small selection of the more conspicuous members of the fauna and the niches they occupy will be considered. First, those that spend most of their time in the canopy. This is where the bulk of the available plant food is to be found, so the majority of animals in this community have to be good climbers or fliers in order to exploit it. The herbivores include nectar feeders, such as sunbirds and butterflies, leaf eaters, ranging in size from colobus monkeys to caterpillars, fruit eaters, including hornbills and bats, and those which rely on a mixture of plant and animal foods, such as blue monkeys and bushbabies. The stricter carnivores are also present, including many insectivorous birds, chameleons, lizards, snakes and praying mantids. Larger carnivores that feed in the canopy are represented by cats such as genets and raptors including the impressive crowned eagle. Parasitic plants and animals are also present.

Some forest mammals

Monkeys are the most conspicuous climbers to be found in forests, and of these, the BLACK AND WHITE COLOBUS is the largest and most acrobatic. It is marvellous to see a troop moving from tree to tree making huge leaps, fur spread out to reduce rate of fall and tail trailing to act as a balancer. Their hands lack a thumb – probably an adaptation for gripping boughs more easily when travelling fast from branch to branch. Each troop has its own 'main roads' through its territory, consisting of a succession of conveniently placed trees where the gaps between boughs are not too wide to be jumped; in this way they avoid having to come down to the ground where they are more vulnerable. They have their favourite roosting and sunning trees which are usually taller than the surrounding ones. Here you can spot them in the early morning warming up in the sunshine before going off to feed; it is worth looking out for them in the forest when returning in the early morning from Mountain Lodge.

Colobus are leaf eaters, but the toxins and cellulose present in the leaves make them difficult to digest. Colobus get over the problem by having a greatly enlarged, two-part stomach which can hold great quantities of leaves and contains symbiotic bacteria. The bacteria serve a dual purpose; they digest the cellulose of the leaves so that the soluble products can be absorbed, and they help to de-activate the toxins.

The **BLUE MONKEY** occupies a different niche, preferring fruits, flowers, buds and shoots – all more easily digested than older leaves; it also takes insects and young birds. In most lights this species looks very black, but with the sun on it, is easily recognised by its bluish-grey mantle and greyish-white eyebrow-stripe above the black face. It is a very acrobatic, arboreal species, living in troops of around 20 animals composed mainly of adult females and their young with usually a single adult male. Troops of non-breeding males also occur. A good place to see them is in the groundwater forest of L. Manyara National Park. Like the common vervet monkeys of woodland and woody savannah, the young are carried under the belly of the mother, clinging to her fur and often coiling their tails around the base of the mother's for extra support.

The **SYKE'S MONKEY** is a sub-species of the blue, and is distinguished by the chestnut saddle and pronounced white ruff. Typically, it occurs at higher altitudes in montane forest, and may commonly be seen near Mountain Lodge, on the slopes of Mt. Kenya and in the bamboo forests of the Aberdares.

All these monkeys are strictly diurnal, but their place is taken at night by other primates – the bushbaby and greater galago. The **BUSHBABY** is adapted for life in the canopy by having well-developed hind limbs for leaping, particularly large eyes for nocturnal vision and a long tail for balance. It also has long fingers, and the toes end in flat discs of thickened skin which help grip. They are extremely agile, moving with a series of erratic leaps from branch to branch with re-markable speed, making it very difficult for a predator such as a genet to catch them.

They feed mainly on insects and fruit, and can detect small prey by using their large ears. These move independently, like those of a serval, and are able to pin-point the source of any sound caused by the movement of the prey. They catch flying insects such as moths by gripping the bough firmly with the hind feet and suddenly thrusting out the body towards the insect, catching it with one or both hands.

They usually have a single baby, which, when only a few days old, is carried by the mother in her mouth and parked nearby while she is feeding; she moves it from one parking place to another as she travels. After about a fortnight the mother rejoins her group, which is composed of a few related females who share a territory. A dominant male's territory is larger than a female's and he may mate with females from more than one group. His reign is often brief as others from a bachelor group are usually eager to challenge his dominance.

They communicate with each other by loud cries and mark their territory wherever they go by employing a strange technique. Using their urine as a scent marker, they periodically smear each hand with a few drops of urine and wipe them on the soles of each foot. In this way their progress is marked by a smelly trail which can be easily recognised.

The **GREATER GALAGO** is a heavier and less agile kind of bushbaby. One may sometimes be seen coming to food after dark at Mountain Lodge. Its diet is rather similar to that of its smaller cousin, but it depends rather more on forest fruits.

The **TREE HYRAX** is another excellent climber. It has short sturdy legs, and the stumpy toes have flattened nails resembling hooves. They are well adapted for climbing as the soles of the feet have rubbery pads well supplied with sweat glands; the sweat helping them to grip. In addition, there are certain muscles present which contract to make a hollow in the centre of the sole which acts as a strong suction cup. On close inspection, the feet look remarkably like an elephant's in miniature, and there are other internal features which also suggest that elephants are indeed their nearest living relatives.

They are nocturnal, spending the day in some hollow tree, ideally, one with several entrance holes. Occasionally you may glimpse one towards the end of the day sitting motionless with its head poking out of a tree hole. They emerge at dusk and quickly climb into the canopy where they start to feed. They are strictly vegetarian, feeding mainly on fruits, leaves, shoots and bark.

In places such as Mountain Lodge or Tree-Tops, you often hear their harsh, blood-curdling screams. It is surprising that so much noise can be made by an animal no bigger than an adult rabbit. It is emitted by both sexes and serves as either a territorial challenge or a sexual contact call.

Many forest mammals eat fruit, but few are fruit-eating specialists, apart from the fruit bats. The latter take the night shift after the diurnal birds and monkeys have had their share. Deep in the Maramagambo forest there is a cave (really a tunnel as it is open at both ends) where 50,000 or more ROUSETTE FRUIT BATS roost by day. This is one of the few species of fruit bat that uses caves for this purpose. Long before we reached the cave the pungent odour told us that it was not far away. As we approached, we could see the roof and walls were crammed with bats, and on entering, they peeled off from their roosting places in their hundreds and whirled around us. The noise was very loud – a high-pitched hissing caused by the combination of a myriad of tiny squeaks. Inside the cave the smell was almost overpowering, and the droppings on the floor covered the loose boulders with a slippery slime. It was astonishing to see such a vast concentration of animals in one small area. Colonies, like these, need an immense amount of food; but fruiting trees are widely spaced in the forest and ripen at different seasons, so to exploit the harvest, the bats on emergence at dusk, may have to travel far to seek out the best trees.

Some forest birds

There are many niches for birds in the forest. Right at the top of the food chain is the CROWNED EAGLE. It is usually seen soaring above the trees as it patrols its large territory, or perched on a bough below the canopy. It is easily recognised by its large size and pronounced double crest. When in flight, it can manoeuvre with ease among the branches of the canopy and in this way may surprise a monkey. Its hunting technique is to fly low over the animal and strike with a blow of its open feet. It will also take animals on the ground such as young bushbuck, red duiker and suni. The nest is easily recognised by its huge size – up to 2 m across, and built in the main fork of a large tree. The same nest is used year after year.

Forest HORNBILLS are specialist fruit-eaters. The huge bill is well adapted for taking all kinds of succulent fruit; large items are sliced by the serrated edges of the mandibles and smaller ones are delicately picked off by the pointed tips. Food is usually swallowed whole and the seeds regurgitated later; an excellent dispersal mechanism. The strange casque on the upper side of the bill is very light in weight due to its spongy, air-filled construction.

Hornbills nest in tree holes, and the male has the engaging habit of imprisoning his mate for the duration of incubation by plastering up the entrance with mud and excrement. He just leaves a vertical slit through which he feeds his mate and the young chicks. This is an excellent strategy for defending the nest against snakes and monkeys. When the young are older, the female is freed, and both birds can share the feeding. The young are fed on insects as well as fruit, the former providing more protein for growth.

TURACOS are also mainly fruit eaters. These large, strikingly coloured birds with prominent crests and long tails are usually noticed when they fly between forest trees. After landing, they move in a most peculiar manner, scuttling along the boughs like squirrels.

WOODPECKERS fill a well-defined niche in the ecosystem. They exploit a food source which other predators cannot easily reach, the wood-boring insects. However, they will also take insects and spiders found on the surface by methodically spiralling up trunks and boughs searching all the nooks and crannies in the bark.

The equipment used for boring into hard wood is both efficient and sophisticated. The bill is strong, straight and pointed and powered by highly-developed neck muscles. You would think that the prolonged hammering would cause a woodpecker to have a bad headache, but the brain is protected by a large skull with very thick walls. When drilling, the rough bark is gripped by the pincer-like claws of the toes which are arranged two in front and two behind to increase efficiency. The short legs allow the body to remain close to the trunk, and extra support is given by the tail feathers which are stiff and strong and act as a prop. When an insect gallery has been opened up, the extraordinarily long, thin tongue is extended to reach the furthest recesses to hook the insect out. To help this difficult operation the tip of the tongue has backwardly projecting barbs and is sticky with saliva.

Woodpeckers also nest in trees, choosing a limb slightly softened by fungal attack to lessen the labour of excavation. They make a tunnel which starts straight and then goes vertically down to a hollowed-out chamber at the base – a good anti-predator device.

CUCKOOS are more easily heard than seen, but they are not uncommon in forests. Like the European species they are nest parasites, laying a single egg in the nest of another bird and leaving the foster parent to rear the chick. The red-chested cuckoo chooses the nest of a robin chat, while the beautiful emerald cuckoo parasitises bulbuls and weaver finches, which nest high in the canopy. When the foster parent leaves the nest, the cuckoo quickly flies in, lays an egg and removes one of the foster parent's. If it times the operation success-fully, the young cuckoo will hatch before the other chicks and is able to evict the other eggs, thus eliminating competition for food. Even if the timing is at fault, the young cuckoo, being bigger, is usually able to heave the other nestlings over the nest's rim.

Other animals of the canopy

Many reptiles make a living here. Tree snakes, which are usually green and very thin, climb with sinuous movements among the branches and explore tree holes for eggs or nestlings, search for tree frogs and hunt for other animals such as chameleons and lizards.

Predator and prey gain much from camouflage, and chameleons are masters of the art. The value of camouflage is greatly enhanced by immobility, and the chameleon's hunting technique is to remain still and wait for insects to come within striking distance, or move incredibly slowly towards the prey. The eyes can swivel in all direc-tions, so body movements can be reduced to a minimum, and when both eyes are focused on the same object, distances can be judged accurately and aim improved. A chameleon's tongue is a remarkable weapon; it is so extensible that it can be extruded with lightning speed for a distance greater than its body length. The end is broad and sticky and wraps around the insect which is flicked back into the mouth. Chameleons bear many young – tiny replicas of their parents. Although quickly abandoned, they are born with the instinctive ability to snap at any insects in the vicinity.

Insects occur in great numbers in the canopy; butterflies visit flowers for nectar and their caterpillars chew the leaves with their strong mandibles. There are also many beetles, crickets, ants, bees and wasps. Some insects, such as praying mantids, are predators on other insects. They are wonderfully disguised to represent leaves and stems and wait motionless, with fore legs at the ready, for an insect to come near. Their large compound eyes enable them to detect a flying insect quickly and gauge its speed and direction. Then, having done so, they make a lightning thrust with the front limbs, grasping the insect in their pincer-like claws. Spiders are also present in the canopy, some spinning webs for the unwary, some lurking in flowers to catch but-terflies which visit them, while others pounce on their prey.

The terrestrial animals

Food near ground level is rather limited for the larger animals, so relatively few species spend their whole lives in dense forest. However, excellent shelter is provided, and large mammals such as elephant, rhino and buffalo frequently utilise this habitat. They use well-worn paths which link up good feeding areas, salt licks and drinking places and will emerge on to more open country, particularly at night, where additional food may be found. At lodges such as Tree Tops, Mountain Lodge or The Ark, it is always a thrill to see a herd of elephants suddenly, and with hardly a sound, materialise from the forest edge as if by magic and make their way to the water hole to drink. Later, after satisfying their thirst they return in single file to be swallowed up once more by the dense vegetation.

There are also species which are true forest animals and particularly well adapted to these conditions; they include two kinds of pig and several species of antelope. The largest of the pigs is the **GIANT FOREST HOG** – about half the size of a buffalo. Strangely, for such a large animal, it was not discovered by scientists until 1904. Although local in distribution, it is commonly seen in the Aberdares, on the slopes of Mt. Kenya and in the forests of Uganda. It likes to wallow in marshy places, and feeds on coarse vegetation including tall grass, shrubs and fallen fruit. It does not dig so much for its food as the other pig species. They are usually seen in small family groups, often led by an old boar.

The **BUSHPIG** is much smaller and more nocturnal. The colour is very variable, but is usually dark or reddish brown with much white in the head region and down the centre of the back, particularly in older animals. They feed on roots, fallen fruits, berries, eggs, young birds and small mammals. The snout is used like a miniature plough in soft earth for turning up edible material and the tusks are used for breaking and extracting tough roots.

I was very surprised to see in the Luangwa Valley a bushpig in the middle of the day associating with a troop of baboons. On enquiry, I was told that this particular animal had often been seen over a three year period, always with these baboons. Associations between different species are common, both parties often benefiting, but an association between a nocturnal animal and a group of diurnal ones is very strange. It would be intriguing to know how this came about.

The forest antelopes have not been well studied, as keeping them under observation is so difficult, but there is no doubt that each species occupies a different niche. This is indicated by their varying sizes which enable them to reach different heights of browse. The bongo, for example, is a large antelope, a bushbuck is of medium height, duikers are small and suni tiny. All have relatively large eyes which help them to cope with twilight conditions in the forest by day and hardly any light at night. They are also well camouflaged with spots and stripes making them well nigh invisible in vegetation in dappled sunshine.

The **BUSHBUCK** is the most commonly seen. As dusk approaches, its tentative emergence from the forest to drink or feed is the personification of caution and alertness. Mainly nocturnal, it prefers to browse on leaves and tender shoots of bushes and young trees. Colour and pattern of spots are very variable, with the bucks often darker than the does; markedly so in those in the Aberdares.

The large size of the **BONGO** requires it to wander far in the forest to find sufficient food. By day it hides up in dense vegetation and at night may occasionally be seen in forest glades and other clearings where browse is more abundant. The visitor is very fortunate to see one, although at one time bongo used to visit salt licks at Tree Tops and The Ark spasmodically during the drier season. Today this is a rare occurrence as most bongo keep to higher altitudes and are extremely shy. The males are mainly solitary, although one is sometimes seen with a group of females and young.

In montane forest the commonest duiker seen is the **RED FOREST DUIKER** (Harvey's). This small antelope is bright chestnut, and like most duikers, has front legs shorter than the hind; this gives it a wedge-shaped appearance, ideal for plunging into thick vegetation at speed. It may sometimes be seen in a clearing or at the forest edge at dusk. I once saw two males having a battle royal near Mountain Lodge. They are remarkably strong for their size and very agile, and their short, sharply pointed horns make effective weapons. Because of the general scarcity of browse at the level they can reach, most of the forest duikers are opportunistic in their feeding, relying considerably on fallen fruit.

The **SUNI** is one of the smallest antelopes – almost hare size, but with longer legs. Those occurring in montane forest are usually seen above 2,500 m. A good place to see them is near The Ark where they come out of the bushes in late day or early morning to feed on nutritious herbs and grasses; however, their main food consists of leaves and young shoots from low shrubs. The montane form is usually dark reddish brown with a rather lighter face and throat; it occurs in pairs or small family parties. There is a gland just below the eye which secretes a strong musky-smelling substance which is rubbed on to vegetation within the territory.

At the top of the food web is the leopard, but no details will be given here as its way of life has already been described in the chapter on the bigger carnivores.

The most conspicuous insect seen on the forest floor is the siafu or safari ant. You may see myriads of these remarkable creatures forming a thick column which snakes its way in an apparently endless stream of scurrying individuals. Those at the front produce a scent trail which all the others instinctively follow. On close inspection, the column is seen to consist of long lines of workers flanked by soldiers with huge jaws. Trying to take close-up photographs is somewhat hazardous as their bites are extremely painful. They will attack anything in their path, alive or dead, and smother it with individuals all intent on dismembering it into small enough portions to be taken back to the nest. Meanwhile, the column travels relentlessly onwards, swarming over dead trunks and crossing small streams by forming living chains which act as a bridge for the army to pass over. To the observer it appears as if the whole column is acting like a single organism with its component parts all acting instinctively and with devastating efficiency – a predator par excellence.

Scavengers and decomposers

Termites are the major scavengers of dead plant material within the forest ecosystem. The nests of some species are very conspicuous as large dark brown structures, often high up trees, fused to a trunk or large bough. Termites have the ability to digest wood and cellulose, turning these substances into sugars which can then be absorbed. In some species this is done with the help of symbiotic protozoa living in the gut. These microscopic organisms, when in excess, may also be digested by the host – a useful source of additional protein. It is rather like culling a species to leave a sustainable residue. Forest termites cause the destruction of dead trees and quicken the process of decay by helping fungi to penetrate hard wood. They also break down the leaf litter along with smaller insects such as springtails.

The humid conditions of the forest are ideal for fungal growth. Toadstools are commonly seen, but these are only the reproductive organs – the conspicuous parts of the fungi. The remainder consists of a network of tiny threads which ramify in dead wood, within the leaf litter and deeper in the soil. These are the feeding portions of the fungus which secrete digestive juices on to the dead material and then absorb the products. Some of these fungi form a remarkable partnership with tree roots, forming a mat of threads around their surfaces through which soluble substances are passed to the benefit of both fungus and tree. This reduces the problem of nutrients, formed during the decay process, being leached out of the soil before the trees can absorb them. Of course, as in all ecosystems, bacteria also play their part in decomposition and the production of further nutrients.

Thus the recycling process within a forest ecosystem follows familiar paths, but there is greater emphasis on the green plant – decomposer – green plant cycle, as only about 10% of the plant products available are eaten by herbivores and pass through the food web in the usual manner. Instead, most of it is either stored away in the wood of great trees for decades and even centuries, or falls to the ground in a constant rain of leaves to add to the litter on the forest floor. In both cases, long term or short, it is the scavengers and decomposers that play the major role.

CHAPTER 15

Africa at Night

It is a thrilling experience to go for a night drive in a National Park. You have the feeling that you are trespassing in a world that belongs to others, a world where nocturnal animals are actively engaged in feeding or hunting, where scent and hearing are more important than the sense of sight which we rely upon so much. You experience a feeling of expectant excitement, all senses alert, not knowing what you will see next. If the chance occurs, it should be taken; it will provide an exciting glimpse of another world.

Sadly, it is not possible for many National Parks to allow visitors to take night drives, but you can do so in some of the more remote parts of East Africa, and in Zambia it is easily arranged. Failing that, you can get an exciting flavour of night life by visiting Tree Tops, Mountain Lodge or The Ark where dim artificial lighting enables you to see the behaviour and interactions of many nocturnal species. Sleeping under canvas is another way of experiencing the thrill of Africa at night. You may not see so much, but intriguing sounds are all around you; it is wonderful to hear from the safety of your tent the distant roar of a lion, the whoops and cackles of hyaenas, or the noisy feeding of hippos as they pluck great mouthfuls of coarse grass when foraging nearby.

If you do have the good fortune to go on a night drive, a spot-light run from the car battery is essential. By sweeping this from side to side while travelling slowly, you quickly pick out the eye reflections of the animals and can stop before they become alarmed. Then, it is best to approach as near as you can without disturbing them, turn off the engine and use a less powerful torch to observe their behaviour. It is surprising how little notice they take under these circumstances. On one occasion we picked up the eyes of a civet, but on getting near, it went into some bushes and we thought that was the end of it; however, we turned off the engine and decided to wait a little. We were fortunate as it soon re-appeared; this time taking no notice of us. Unfortunately, it made its way towards an area which was too wet for us to follow, so as a last resort I made some squeaks with my mouth against the back of my hand. It stopped, listened intently, and then came trotting across. When it reached the vehicle it smelt the front wheel carefully, but getting no satisfaction from that, it must have decided that there was better hunting elsewhere as it slowly went on its way, scenting and listening for any signs of prey. It was a rewarding experience to see a civet from such close quarters.

You soon learn to recognise many species by their eye reflections before you get close enough to see other details. The main points of difference are the colour, relative size, distance apart, height from the ground, whether you see one at a time or always two, and the pattern made by the eyes when the animal moves, either keeping horizontal or gently moving up and down.

Hippo's eyes reflect red and are small, spaced far apart and are seen well off the ground. If the eyes are at first-storey height, rather small and either single or very far apart, they obviously belong to an elephant. A buffalo's eyes appear white or greenish, and as they are herd animals which face you when disturbed, the sweep of the light picks out a long line of paired reflections like a distant view of a line of street lights. The various species of antelopes all show rather similar, silvery-white reflections; their eyes are large and you usually only see one at a time because they look at you when their heads are sideways-on, and when they walk, the eyes move gently up and down with their neck movement.

A lion's eyes, like those of other cats, reflect a golden colour, and a hyaena's are very bright white, are near together, rather large and about a metre from the ground: almost invariably you see them in pairs as they have a fair degree of binocular vision. The eyes of genets, civets and white-tailed mongooses all give relatively large, golden reflections which are very close together. A genet's eyes are almost level with the ground unless it is climbing, but a civet keeps its head higher when moving.

When doing a night drive, it is good to take a route which goes through a variety of habitats as you are then likely to see more species. When near trees, search the boughs with the spot-light, as it is here that bushbabies may be found. The bright reflections from their large eyes, set close together, are easily picked out, and as you watch, the eyes appear to dance about among the foliage as the animal leaps nimbly among the branches. Wooded areas are also good for seeing some of the middle-sized carnivores; genets are usually the most common, but in some districts you may be lucky enough to see a ratel foraging amongst the ground vegetation.

Keep an eye on the track in front of you as you move slowly forward. A solitary pink eye which occasionally winks at you and is seen at ground level will almost certainly belong to a nightjar. These curious-looking birds settle on the ground between flights: you have to be very careful not to run them down as they leave it until the last moment before taking off. Nightjars feed on insects, and may frequently be seen hawking for moths at places such as Samburu, where lights from the lodge pick out their pale wings as they fly erratically over the surface of the river after their prey.

Another bird sometimes seen standing tall in the middle of a track is Verreaux's eagle owl. You wonder what it can possibly be until you get close, as it hardly looks like a bird when standing upright and nearly a metre high. With binoculars, it is possible to see its unusual, pink eyelids – looking almost as if it had used make-up.

When driving through areas of thick grass, it is not unusual to put up quail. These tiny game-birds fly up from the grass as you approach, and hover like giant moths in the headlights before flying on and flopping down into the grass again.

The spotted stone curlew, or dikkop, is another bird you see more often at night. Its mottled plumage makes it most inconspicuous by day, but at night, when it is much more active, it is easily picked up by the beam of the spot-light. Its large eyes, adapted for night vision, are very conspicuous.

Water holes and marshy areas are excellent places to visit on a night drive, especially after rain when frogs and toads are in good voice. You can tell water is not far off long before you reach it by the cacophony of sounds which greet you, and with the help of the light, you can search out the members of the orchestra. Three or four species may be present, each with its characteristic notes ranging from the deep base of the bullfrogs to the piping trebles of some of the smaller kinds. The males balloon-up their vocal sacs at each side of the throat when making these noises.

The highlight of a night drive is when you see one of the big cats. Both leopard and lion are more active by night, so you have a very good chance of seeing them in action. I remember one occasion in Kafue National Park in Zambia when a leopard crossed the track in front of the vehicle. It quickly disappeared into the darkness, but as we were overlooking a valley, by using the powerful spot-light we were able to scan the area we thought it was making for. Far over, we picked up a mass of eyes from a large herd of antelope, almost certainly impala. We watched, wondering what would happen. Then, suddenly the eyes started to dance like sparks in a firework display. Clearly, the approaching leopard had caused panic amongst the antelopes which had leapt in all directions and fled. Unfortunately, on this occasion it was impossible to get nearer to see whether the leopard had been successful in its hunt. An anticlimax? Not really, Africa at night is full of the half-seen and the incompletely understood – that is part of the magic.

Lion resting under the shade of a tree at mid-day is one thing, but when you find them on a kill at night it is quite another. It is possible to get quite close to lion under these circumstances without worrying them, as they are far too intent on their feeding; this can be very exciting. On one occasion in Ruwenzori National Park we came upon fifteen lion feeding on the remains of an old bull buffalo. They made a compact circle round the carcase, each with its head within reach of some part of the body. The noise of their feeding was punctuated by angry growls and gruff protests when one poached on another's preserves; there was much scrunching of bone, and party manners were conspicuous by their absence. Occasionally one of the bigger animals would get up and force its way into another part of the circle where the feeding was better.

After some hours, most were full to capacity, and one by one they retreated a few yards to sleep it off, leaving the carcase to the younger ones which had not done so well. Lions were sprawled over the grass in various states of satiation, some were asleep, others were rolling on their backs from side to side, apparently too full to settle down. One lioness, discovering that the front wheel of our vehicle made an admirable back rest, flopped down beside it and went fast asleep. This was nice for the lioness, but it made it difficult for us to make our get-away without disturbing her dreams. For the remainder of this chapter I will consider in more detail the life styles of some of the commoner nocturnal mammals

Genet

These graceful, long-bodied, short-legged hunters are not related to cats, but to civets and mongooses. They hide up by day in hollow trees, old termite mounds, unoccupied warthog holes or in rock crevices. They may even seek the shelter of an abandoned eagle's or hammerkop's nest as they are superb climbers. At night, they venture out to hunt roosting birds, rodents, shrews, bushbabies, frogs, millipedes and the larger insects, and they will take fruit as well. They prefer areas of dense vegetation and are as much at home in the forest canopy as on the ground.

Their hunting technique is to combine a stealthy approach with a lightning-quick pounce, sometimes leaping into the air to claw down a fleeing bird. By being a solitary hunter success is enhanced. The spotted coat gives them good camouflage when stalking and the long ringed tail acts as an excellent balancer when leaping. All senses are acute – large eyes, adapted for night conditions and set close together to give binocular vision, quite large, mobile ears for direction-finding, coupled with superb hearing, a good sense of smell, and an array of long touch-sensitive whiskers.

Genets lead a solitary life, social interactions being confined to mating and rearing young. The females are territorial and defend their ranges against other members of the same sex, but males wander more freely. They use a variety of vocalisations and are able to purr like cats, but their main means of communication is by scent, using urine, faeces and secretions from the perineal glands. When scent marking with these glands, they squat on objects at ground level, or make hand-stands to reach taller structures.

Genets become mature when two years old and bring up their 2–4 young in some hidden refuge; often a hollow tree or an old termite mound. They are commonly seen around lodges and readily come to food put out for them. Visitors to Samburu Lodge may occasionally see one running on the beams of the dining hall after most people have finished their evening meal.

Civet

The civet is larger and longer-legged than the genet and has a much shorter tail. Although both species may be found in the same habitats, particularly savannah and forest, the civet also favours places which genets visit less frequently, such as reed beds and cultivated areas. Competition is further reduced by differences in hunting technique, not climbing like a genet and being more of an opportunistic forager than a hunter. It is also more omnivorous, eating fallen fruit and other vegetable products as well as animals such as spring-hares, rodents, game-birds, millipedes and a variety of insects, especially beetles.

Civets defaecate at special middens, known as civetries which are often situated on the boundaries between territories. Well-established civetries may cover a square metre or more and contain many piles of droppings. Even a superficial examination of the dung tells you quite a lot about what the local civets have been eating. One civetry I looked at in the South Luangwa National Park illustrated well the opportunistic nature of their foraging as it contained the chitinous rings of giant millipedes, many beetle elytra, including those of large scarabs, a few feathers and some hard seeds, possibly those of the African ebony tree.

When alarmed or molested, a civet will raise its crest (which consists of a narrow band of long hairs along the middle of the back) and fluff out its rough coat so that it appears much bigger than it really is.

Civets are seldom seen by day as they spend the daylight hours in burrows or thickets, emerging only at night-fall. Like genets, they live solitary lives, communicating with other civets largely by scent. Their perineal glands are large muscular sacs containing a copious supply of a secretion which emits a powerful, disagreeable smell. This substance is used for marking objects within the territory, such as trees which provide supplies of fallen fruit, or places where a particular food resource is easily available. When following trails, they scent-mark at frequent intervals, smearing objects along the way with pungent messages about individuality, sex and sexual condition. It is not only civets that benefit from this secretion, as humans have used it for centuries as a fixative for flower perfumes. Used at low concentrations, it enhances these scents and renders them remarkably long-lasting. Civets become mature during their second year and may have two litters of 1–3 young a year.

White-tailed mongoose

The long, furry white tail of this mongoose is its most conspicuous feature. When you catch a glimpse of one on a fairly dark night it is often the only part of the animal you see, as the body itself is dark and inconspicuous. You get the weird impression of a disembodied, elongated, white object moving quickly just above the ground.

One of my first encounters with this species was on a night drive. When we picked up its eye reflections, we were at first unsure of the identity of the animal as it was snaking its way through dense grass. We followed it as it ran fast in front of us, and only when it crossed an open space could we identify it clearly in the headlights. When we got closer, it jumped high in the air several times, twisting and twirling its long white tail as it did so. This made it look much more conspicuous and at the same time a lot bigger than it actually was. This pattern of behaviour may act as a warning to any pursuing predator. This species also possesses anal glands which secrete a vile-smelling fluid capable of putting any carnivore off its meal.

The white-tailed mongoose is a true generalist. It feeds opportunistically on a great variety of foods, both animal and vegetable. It will take many insects such as termites, beetles, grasshoppers and caterpillars, searching for them on vegetation, in the dung of the larger herbivores and in the ground by digging. It will also eat rodents, ground-nesting, or roosting birds and their eggs, lizards and snakes and fallen fruits of many kinds. It will also scavenge on carrion and any scraps that can be found near habitation.

The 2–4 young are born in some safe retreat such as a burrow vacated by another species. Like all the mongooses, the young are very playful and a delight to watch.

Ratel (honey badger)

Ratels may occasionally be seen during the day, usually when travelling, or by their dens, but they are mainly active at night. They are sometimes seen around safari camps or lodges where food scraps are regularly put out. Samburu, Amboseli and some of the lodges in the South Luangwa National Park are good places to look out for them, but they are of much greater interest when seen behaving more naturally when you are on a night drive.

They are stocky, low-slung animals with extremely strong necks and limb muscles. The skin is loose, rubbery and very thick, especially in the neck where it can be a good 6 mm. Here it protects the vital jugular veins from damage during fights with other ratels.

Their extraordinary colouring, silvery above and black below, probably acts as a warning; the message being 'keep off and mind your own business or there will be trouble'. If you see a ratel on a fairly dark night, the silver shows up, but the lower parts are invisible, giving the strange illusion, when the animal moves, of a silvery object floating uncannily above the surface of the ground.

The ratel has a well-earned reputation for fearlessness and aggression, and if young are present in the den, will attack anything which comes near. When it bites an animal larger than itself, it holds on to it with great tenacity however much it thrashes about, and has been known to hold on until the aggressor collapses with fatigue. Large animals are not attacked as a potential food source.

Their very varied diet includes porcupines, smaller rodents, hares, young antelopes, ground-nesting birds, snakes, lizards and tortoises. They will also raid crocodile nests and occasionally eat fruit, but the larger insects are their main food, particularly bees, termites and dung beetles.

Bees' nests often occur in hollow trees, and ratels have a special technique for obtaining them. When the bees are disturbed, they will attack with great fury, but the ratel responds by squirting anal gland secretion to subdue them. This nauseating substance acts rather like an anaesthetic, causing them to become dopey. The ratel then tears away at the bark with its powerful claws to expose the nest and gulps down the comb containing honey and larvae. It is not immune to stings, but its thick hide gives it some protection.

There is a well-known association between the ratel and the black-throated honey-guide, a bird not uncommon in bushy savannah. This bird searches diligently for bees' nests as it likes to feed on the larvae and wax of the comb, but it is seldom able to reach the nest on its own. It may then seek out a ratel and attract its attention by repeatedly calling, swooping and displaying the white of its tail. The ratel then follows the bird to the tree containing the bees' nest and attempts to expose it. If successful, it eats most of the comb itself, but there is always enough remaining for the bird to have its share.

Anal gland secretion is not only used to quieten ferocious insects, but also serves to mark features within its extensive home range. As in other carnivores, the scent acts like a news sheet providing information about the sex, status and identity of the animal.

The 1–4 young, blind and nearly naked, are born in a grass-lined nest below ground. Their eyes open at around five weeks and they first emerge from the den when 2–3 months old.

Porcupine

The crested porcupine is the species most often seen in East Africa. It is a very large rodent weighing up to 25 kg and is so named because it has an upstanding crest of long backwardly-curved hairs on head, neck and shoulders. Most of the upper parts of the body are covered in long, black and white, pointed quills and the short tail is surrounded by stouter quills with a cluster of shorter ones at the tip which rattle when the tail is shaken. If approached by a predator such as lion or leopard, or even a slowly approaching vehicle, a porcupine will raise its spines, rattle its tail quills and make menacing noises. It may follow this up by suddenly backing on to its attacker leaving some of its spines embedded in its skin. This can be very painful, and although the spines are not poisonous, they are difficult to dislodge and the wounds often become septic. However, many are killed by predators.

Porcupines are vegetarians, feeding on a variety of plant material, including roots, bulbs and fruits of many kinds, and near villages they may do damage to cultivated crops – they have a particular liking for roots and potatoes. Like all rodents, they use their prominent incisors to gnaw their food, large objects being held firmly with their fore paws while being eaten. They may have to roam far to find enough suitable food, so home ranges are extensive.

Mating provides the male with a prickly problem, but when the female is receptive, she raises her rump and tail and the male stands nearly upright with his fore paws on her back. Between one and three young are born underground in a burrow system, the nest chamber being lined with grass. At birth the young are already well developed with eyes open and soft quills already projecting through the skin. The quills harden within a few days and grow rapidly. Very soon, the young are able to follow the mother when she goes foraging.

Spring-hare

This extraordinary looking rodent is the clown of the dry savannah. When you first come across a group of them at night, all you see are their eye reflections dancing erratically as the animals jump in all directions. On closer inspection, spring-hares look like miniature kangaroos with hare-like ears and a long tail which has a dark brush at the tip. They are as large as hares, rufous brown above, paler on the flanks and white below. The strong hind legs and feet are greatly elongated, giving very effective leverage for jumping, and the toes end in sharp claws which help them to get a good grip when hopping at speed. In contrast, the fore paws are short and not used at all while hopping, but when resting or feeding, the animal goes on all-fours like a rabbit.

Spring-hares are strictly nocturnal, spending the day in extensive burrow systems. Although a number of individuals form burrows in the same area, these are not connected and each has its own domain: they are not social to any degree. They are well adapted for digging. The strong, short, fore paws armed with five sharp claws enable them to dig rapidly in sandy soils, but with such ungainly back legs the tunnels need to be quite large to allow free movement. When digging, the ears are automatically closed by a muscular inner lobe which prevents dust from entering. When a spring-hare returns to its burrow, it closes the door behind it by blocking the entrance with soil from the inside.

Spring-hares may have to go long distances to find enough food, particularly during the dry season. Grasses are their mainstay, but they will dig for succulent roots and bulbs and eat the leaves of herbaceous plants.

They have many predators, including caracal, jackal and the giant eagle owl, but their speedy, erratic movements enable them to reach their burrows remarkably fast. Another anti-predator device they use is to feed as a group so that their combined alertness gives them early warning of danger. Their senses are very acute: the eyes are large and well-adapted for night vision, and project from the side sufficiently far for them to see directly behind without turning the head, and hearing and their sense of smell are also very good.

Their reproductive strategy is to invest in small numbers and look after them well. Mature females have only one young at a time, but there is a long gestation, and when born, the baby is quite large. It is suckled in the safety of the burrow and does not venture above ground until seven weeks old, when nearly as big as its mother. By then, it is already well equipped to face danger, so losses are kept low. Once the juvenile is independent, the mother mates again. Thus her adult life becomes a sequence of pregnancies and lactations, one young being born every three months. What a life!

In this book I have attempted to draw a picture of inter-relationships within ecosystems; how each kind of living organism fills a particular niche for which it is uniquely adapted. The picture does no more than hint at the beauty of this fragile, complex, dynamically-changing whole, held together by a myriad of interacting species. Built up over millions of years, shaped by climatic changes and catastrophic earth movements, and modified by competition for available resources, it has become what we now marvel at – a magnificent panorama of life forms; something to be cherished as a gift of infinite value and safeguarded for all time.

Index

Entries in bold denote major sections for that entry